D1478328

Music Therapy
in action

Music Therapy
in action

MARY PRIESTLEY

ST. MARTIN'S PRESS
NEW YORK

To
Dr E. G. Wooster

Contents

Contents

Foreword

One of the purposes of this book is to stimulate others to do the necessary research and detailed enquiry needed to write the scientific book that this volume does not pretend to be. Another is to help to bring back into public awareness this oldest of healing arts, not as some kind of fringe medicine, but as a valuable ancillary therapeutic service worthy of serious study and attention in its own right. A third purpose is to answer some of the many questions asked in impossible moments, such as "What happens in music therapy? What do patients do? How does it work? Who benefits from it?".

In order to explain how the different music therapy techniques can work in practice, it has been necessary for me to describe actual incidents in the lives and treatment of various clients and patients. In every case the descriptions of these people have been disguised so that only the people concerned, their psychiatrists and myself would recognise them. I have worked in several psychiatric hospitals and the impressions of ward sessions have been re-created from notes from a number of sessions. In a way this gives the reader a truer overall picture of a session than any one meticulously accurate description of a single hour on the ward.

I offer grateful thanks to all the authors and publishers from whom I have taken quotations, to Juliette Alvin whose steadfast vision enabled her to found the British Society for Music Therapy and start the Music Therapy Diploma course at the Guildhall School of Music and Drama, to Dr R. de Alarcon for his encouragement, to Dr C. Lindsay for his help in chapter 21, to my colleagues Gillian Lovett, Marjorie Wardle, and Peter Wright for their support and advice, to the patients and clients whose inner music I have been privileged to share, to my father J. B. Priestley and to Dr E. G. Wooster, consultant psychotherapist, for looking through the manuscript and for making suggestions, to the long-suffering victims of my down-graded domestic priorities and to my negative life experiences which have goaded me forward.

Introduction

Apart from some brief contact with music therapy whilst working in the USA, I had not taken seriously into account the potentiality of music as a working tool until I found myself working in a hospital with a well-established music therapy department. Throughout my previous experience in psychiatry and psychotherapy, I had – like many of my colleagues – enjoyed music as one of my chief means of relaxation. Consequently the weekly hospital meetings and other contacts initiated with the music and art therapists depicted in this book have been a stimulating challenge, forcing us to discover the points of similarity between our different disciplines. In the three years that we have been meeting, we have generated considerable enthusiasm for this search. Investigating the use of music and art as complementary and additional modes of expression to the words of psychotherapy, we have seen how sounds, forms, colours or words can be the vehicles that convey feelings within the deeper dialogue that is the essence of therapy. I think, therefore, that this book represents a challenge both to those involved in the mainstream of psychotherapeutic practice and to those who have hitherto seen music merely as a source of enjoyable relaxation, to consider this fresh dimension of its application.

Within this vast subject I have chosen some crucial ideas which are currently receiving attention and these can be seen in an interesting and intriguing new light viewed from the standpoint of music therapy.

Dr D. Winnicott, particularly in his last book *Playing and Reality*, opened our eyes to the importance of play in the emotional development of the individual. The fullest development of each aspect of a human being – intellectual, physical, emotional or sexual – is made possible by allowing him to experience the necessary exploratory period before his arrival at the point of full adult commitment. Indeed, the psychotherapeutic process – whether individual or in a group – may usefully be regarded as an encounter-situation, a playground in which to experience, in the present, that which was

11

lost or missed out in the past. The improvisation of music together seems particularly apt when viewed in the light of this developmental process. The text describes ways in which various kinds of feeling can be expressed symbolically within the musical dialogue.

I would particularly draw attention to the Psychodynamic Movement and Relaxation sessions described in chapter 9. Compared with the East, with its development of Hatha Yoga, concentration on physical sensations and expressive movements has been largely neglected in Western tradition (at least until the recent vogue for physical contact within encounter groups). In the history of psychiatric treatment, relaxation therapy has enjoyed scant support, though it has had its enthusiastic adherents, such as Drs J. H. Schultz, D. H. Fink and E. Jacobson. However, it plays a substantial part in the setting of psychoanalysis and in much behaviour therapy. In these movement sessions, the links between feeling, physical movement and sensation are explored in a way that is just as important as the investigation of the connections between feelings and words, via sound, in analytical music therapy. This is reminiscent of the vital role that ballet has played in music, complementing the art forms of *lieder* and opera.

The techniques described in chapters 14–16 seem to me to be also very much worth considering. First of all as a creative application of Melanie Klein's writing on primary schizoid mechanisms in the development of the psyche (for many of us the most helpful fundamental contribution to the understanding of the dynamics of the psychotic states). Secondly, because we who work in this field so often view our more disturbed patients simplistically: as either wholly mad or at least as living demonstrations of some severe mental illness. Such a view can prevent the helpful sorting out of the confused situation within the patient, where the healthy aspects of his personality may be attempting to come to terms with the disturbed or ill parts. These "mad" parts – and I don't think that these are exclusive to overtly psychotic patients – may be dissociated impulses or perceptions, groundless fears, or bodily symptoms on the one hand, or out of touch, rigid defensive structures on the other. Many patients have found it very comforting, even if painful, to be initiated into a form of musical dialogue with these frightening and hitherto unrecognised parts of themselves. After sorting out the confusions and the personality-splits enough to be able to choose the most appropriate form for the musical improvisation, the music therapist himself takes on the role of the patient's warring feelings in their musical dialogue. In the Splitting technique, where therapist and patient take turns at being subject and object, the therapist uses the patient's artificial projection to bring the disowned feeling back into the patient's awareness and afterwards they discuss the reactions to this.

It is of great value to patients, in my opinion, to know something of the characteristics of their disturbances – however serious. I do not think, generally speaking, that enough attention is paid to this, although in many cases this is only possible, or even appropriate, in the patient's recovery phase. Unfortunately, in psychiatric hospitals, the shortage of staff time and the effort to give general relief all round too often combine to create an attitude of "let sleeping dogs lie". If time could somehow be found to mobilise this potential reflective capacity in each patient, at least some of them could eventually learn to recognise their own internal danger points. When the possibilities of the creative aspect of a breakdown are not accepted by those caring for patients, a serious price may have to be paid for keeping so much unrealised potential locked away through the fear of the possible consequence of its expression. The reader will certainly find some added grounds for this view in this book.

Carrying out the techniques of analytical music therapy is not as easy as it may sound. Many psychotic reactions are based on a denial of that which is painful in the outer or inner world. A great many neurotics, too, would rather keep their phobic, obsessional or psychosomatic mechanisms – to name but a few – rather than trade them in for the deep anxieties and guilts which lie hidden beneath them.

The naive therapeutic enthusiast, who succeeds in prising open a person's defences in order to let their repressed anger or sexuality have an airing by musical, verbal or any other means, is likely to be given a bloody nose – metaphorically or actually – resulting in the patient's exacerbated need to say "I told you so" as he reinforces his defences even more strongly. Such a patient feels (often unconsciously) that since, in the past, his attempts to express himself were punished or went unrewarded, he is going to need to experience his attempts in the here-and-now very differently in order to allow himself to question his previous assumptions about the results of self-expression. This would be true in any therapeutic situation, including that of music therapy.

Therefore, given a patient with some basic motivation for treatment, his potential ability to emerge freely from his defensive shell (with the consequent allowing of more play to his instinctive impulses) should result in real emotional growth. But what is vital here is the therapist's capacity to facilitate this, which demands first and foremost his ability to support the patient and contain the emotion, together with the backing of a helpful environment during the period of treatment, and only secondly his appropriate interpretation or diagnostic skill.

However, even with a good-enough setting in human terms, there will always be clients who will have an infinite capacity to take the therapy "for a ride" in achieving little or no change. For the above reasons, the therapist has two things to consider with regard to his work. First there is the question of how far his own emotional state can allow him to take on the necessary therapeutic burden of his patient's symptoms, often over a long span of time. Secondly, there is the problem of helping to find or create a supporting situation in which the therapist can work at a reasonable level of anxiety, in which he can make experiments and even be allowed to make the occasional mistakes from which he, and his colleagues, can learn so much.

Mary Priestley's book describes explorations that she has made in largely uncharted waters. Moreover, there is a singular lack of any external appreciation of the intrinsic value of such a contribution in this country at present. The dual qualifications necessary for this discipline receive a financial reward of less than half of that normally earned by either a plain musician or therapist in practice.

Long-term assessment of the results achieved – particularly in individual analytical music therapy – will be vital, as these techniques are still very much in the melting-pot. I hope that the opportunity for research arising from this work will soon be taken up. However, this should not detract, at this point in time, from the verve and enjoyment that the reader can share in Mary Priestley's explorations with wards, small groups and in the consulting room.

E. G. WOOSTER, MB, DPM, MRCPsych.

1. What is music therapy?

More than a profession. Scarcely a living. A way of being, of relating at both non-verbal ends of the speech scale: sub-vocal relationship at the fumbling pre-ego depth of being and supra-vocal communication at altitudes where words no longer suffice.

It is rejection and relegation to the file of "Quackery and Witchcraft" in some circles. It is a warm welcome into the multi-disciplinary medical team in others. It is toiling round institution wards with baskets of percussion instruments and bags of music wondering how your muscles will adjust to playing Bach's *Air on a G String* when you reach your destination. It is long hours at night arranging a movement from Beethoven's *Choral Symphony*, on request, for piano, trombone, soprano and cello, only to find next day that the trombonist has been discharged and the cellist transferred to another hospital. It is exploration and astonishment. Frustration and delight. But always it is music and people. It is my life, and I love it.

There are almost as many different kinds of music therapy as there are therapists. Music therapy is an art and, as such, a very personal and creative form of work. Therapists' techniques are built up to meet the needs of their clients and to accommodate their own strengths and weaknesses. But the three main activities involved in music therapy are either musical sound expression on instruments or with the voice, movement to music, or listening to carefully selected music with the therapist. There must be three factors involved in this discipline: the client, the music and the therapist. Where there are only two: the client and the music, the experience may be therapeutic but there is no therapy in the sense of "taking care of or healing". Human relationship is an essential ingredient for this. But one must not underestimate the power of music, which activates the one who improvises or performs, as Vaughan Williams suggested when he wrote: "Music is the reaching out towards the utmost realities by means of ordered sound." To reach out only for records or cassettes is to cheat oneself of a profound inner experience of strengthening growth.

WHAT IS MUSIC THERAPY TO THE CLIENT?

For the severely subnormal child it can be a shared world of sound allowing her to express feelings which she may never be able to communicate in words, through movement to music and perhaps on an instrument. For the autistic child it can be the one communication which he does not shut out, a bridge into the incommunicable regions of his puzzling personality, from which an echo comes back.

For the psychiatric patient – I will let some of them speak for themselves. A woman who had been a patient in a psychiatric hospital for nearly twenty years before leaving to live outside, wrote, "When one is burning in hell, heaven is the wind in one's face. May I say that music therapy is a little like that."

A university-trained widowed mother, with a manic-depressive illness which brought her back to hospital from time to time, wrote, "Music therapy gave me a complete change of air and scene. One forgot about the illness all around and could enjoy something which transcends the present world. The music room might be packed full of people but there was always a wonderful atmosphere there."

A girl just entering her twenties with a metabolic disease and psychological complications wrote, "When I went into hospital I was completely turned inwards and away from society, but due to the warmth and perseverance of the music therapists and the music classes offered to me, I gradually became involved in my environment again. The freedom and joy of being able to express all my pent-up fear and genuine horrors to music and through dancing brought me to confidence and hope."

A family man with a psychosomatic complaint, who was having analytical music therapy, put it rather less tenderly: "When I first came in here and saw these drums and things I thought to myself, 'This is a load of rubbish which is not going to do anything for anybody.' But I'll try anything once, and it worked for me. If anyone asks me how it works I can't tell them. I just say 'You have to try it for yourself.' "

MUSIC AND MEDICINE

From studying the cathartic and hypnotic uses of music in group settings in contemporary primitive tribes, from reading about the temple of Apollo, god of music and medicine, at Delphi and tales of the drumming healers of India and from looking at the cave-drawings of musical shamans dating back to the early palaeolithic times, one can imagine that music must always have been used therapeutically.

16

What is music therapy?

But it is only in the past decade that music therapy has been officially accepted in this country as an ancillary medical service. Today's musician is having to turn his mind from technique, tone colour and harmony to the difficult conceptual models of modern psychologists and psychiatrists. There follow some brief points of contact between our work and theirs, though I realise that each point could well fill a book on its own.

MUSIC THERAPY AND BEHAVIOUR THERAPY

In music therapy music itself is the reward that produces the altered behaviour. A child could be taught to play a simple instrument by operant conditioning methods, the therapist shaping up the required responses and offering rewards when the desired actions were performed. But this would hardly have the healing – and I use healing in the old sense of making whole – the healing quality of letting the child be led by its own curiosity and delight to express itself in sound, while being contained within the warm relationship with the music therapist.

For certain patients music can be used effectively in their desensitisation to phobic objects. Music has the power to retain close associations with the state of mind the subject was in at the time of hearing it. Young couples who adopt a popular song as "our tune" can find the associations painfully difficult to break when their relationship falls apart. Similarly music can be used to recall the feeling of deep relaxation. If – for example – a cat-phobic patient is brought into a state of deep relaxation several times to a certain serene melody, the therapist can then build up tolerance to the idea of the animal's presence. The cat would be first imagined far away, with the music holding the relaxation, and at last, after some successful sessions with the cat being imagined as coming closer, it would be curled up beside her. The memory of the melody can be a help towards reviving the state of deep relaxation when the patient leaves hospital, acting as a booster to cat tolerance.

In some hospitals for the severely subnormal in the United States, patients who cannot understand speech have been conditioned to get ready for bed, to prepare to go to the lavatory, and to enter and leave the dining area in response to specific music which is only used at the appropriate times. This is not, strictly speaking, music therapy but music therapists have been used in the original individual conditioning programme.

What is music therapy?

MUSIC THERAPY LINKING WITH CONCEPTS OF FREUD, ADLER, JUNG AND KLEIN

Music therapy harmoniously integrates the workings of the Ego, Super-Ego and Id of Freud's conceptual model of the psyche. The Id's pleasure orientation can be satisfied (at least partially) by the free expression in sound of the emotions concerned with its urges and desires. The Ego's reality principle is satisfied because an ordered physical form is given to the impulses. The Super-Ego's moralistic orientation is satisfied because making music in this way is a socially accepted and approved activity.

Performing music requires all the four functions of the psyche described by Jung: thinking, to turn the notes into music; feeling, to give it expression; sensation, in the musician's proprioceptive (position awareness) feedback from his body when playing his instrument or singing; and intuition, to get into the very essence of the composer's inspiration.

The musician must be introverted in his search for the deeper meaning of the music which must be found also within himself, and extraverted in performance. Music allows a man to get in touch with and express his "anima" (feminine aspect of a man's unconscious) and a woman to do the same with her "animus". A good therapist will be able to tell whether a client is plumbing the depths of her feelings in playing or merely using the "persona" (the role or character mask with which one faces the world).

Group drumming experiences can bring players into touch with deep levels of the collective unconscious as can folk dance music from their ethnic group.

With regard to Adler's thinking, an individual's will-to-power can better be satisfied by performing music and using her emotions to promote a useful life-style than by crippling herself with them and dominating others by invalidism.

In Melanie Klein's conceptualisation the earliest phase of the infant's psychic development is called the paranoid-schizoid position. At this stage a splitting takes place when the baby divides his experience of his mother, who is termed his primary object, into a good part and a bad part and thus feels that this part is persecuting him by reflecting and pushing back into him all his angry reactions to his experiences of hunger, pain and isolation. In music therapy such states of mind can be explored in sound by the client and therapist improvising together and taking it in turns to express feelings about each part in sounds and then words.

18

The next, more integrated stage of development Melanie Klein describes as the depressive position. At this stage the child can tolerate both good and bad parts of what the object can offer and reflect. By being able to accept both sides of the object inside the self, the child then achieves toleration of ambivalent feelings towards it. He can begin to appreciate his mother's reality as it is including her distressing capacity to come and go of her own volition.

A client having difficulty in the toleration of ambivalent feelings for one person, and thus struggling to keep her objects as idealised characters or villains, can often first begin to tolerate these warring feelings while expressing them in sound with the therapist. Her subsequent desire to make reparation for the expressed hate can be guided into a pleasurable life-affirming sound-improvisation duet. But it takes time and patience to achieve these results.

Music therapy permits what the analyst discourages: the acting out of the emotions. But with music this is done with some control through the guilt-free medium of non-verbal sound. Feelings which are beneath the level of consciousness can rise to the surface with great force when they can be contained by a sound matrix. Such feelings, by the force of their physical expression, overwhelmingly convince the client that they are there. The analytical music therapist (see chapter 3) then has the task of tying them up with understanding and realisation in words. In analysis the process is often reversed. The analyst's interpretation exposes the unconscious emotive situation, which is not consciously experienced or admitted by the analysand, and it may be several hours, days or even months before she feels it burst upon her as an emotional reality. Sometimes the resistances are so great that it never happens.

An analytical music therapist will feel most at home working mentally within the conceptual model used by his own analyst or analytical psychotherapist. But in collecting ideas to base the musical techniques on, he is eclectic. As brief examples: from the active imagination process used by Jungians to follow the intimations of a personal myth from the patient's unconscious, we get the guided imagery improvisations. From the originally Freudian recounting of dreams and the associations involved come the improvisations on dreams. From the Kleinian idea of splitting of objects come the improvisations where therapist and client take turns to play the two sides of a conflicting situation either split in an intra-psychic way (though the client may be projecting this and experiencing it externally) or between the subject and an object.

It is difficult to describe music therapy in any way that will give the reader the understanding which I would like to convey. Perhaps the rest of the book will fill up the gaps.

Part One

Preparation

2. Training and improvisation

CONDITIONS OF ENTRY
The LGSM (Music Therapy) is a post-graduate qualification. It stands for Licentiateship of the Guildhall School of Music and Drama. In order to enter this full-time one-year Diploma course, the musician must first of all have completed a full-time three-year course of musical training and successfully passed an examination such as the ARCM, LRAM or GRSM. When I enrolled it was the rule that in some cases – my own was one – a lengthy period of performing and teaching might be accepted as a substitute proof of musical competence.

Great emphasis is placed on the musician possessing the "right personality". In her book *Music Therapy*, Juliette Alvin (founder of the course at the Guildhall and also the British Society for Music Therapy) writes,

> The personal qualities needed to succeed in the field are numerous, some are essential. They include a stable, mature personality, the ability to communicate, to share and to observe, to show warm sympathy and understanding without becoming emotionally involved, to have a sense of humour, to be patient and tolerant whatever happens.

I imagine that some of us must have been deemed adequate on the unspoken proviso that "only five of these need be attempted". I would add to this list: imagination, intuition, creativity and adaptability without which a music therapist soon ossifies. These qualities were judged at the preliminary interviews with Mme Alvin and a course teacher, and again at the musical audition with the Principal of the Guildhall. There was careful enquiry into motivation.

THE EXAMINATION
In the year in which I studied, the course was very well balanced with plenty of practice in writing (essays and case notes), performing on first and second study instruments, practical music therapy,

23

speaking and group participation (in seminars and tutorials), improvisation and listening. A good two-thirds of the course was psychological rather than musical.

At the final performance and musicianship examinations I played the second and third movements of Bach's *Violin Concerto in A Minor* and the first and second movements of the Brahms *Violin Sonata in G Major* and was asked to do some sight-reading. On the piano I played from memory Handel's *Allegro from the Seventh Suite* and two waltzes by Brahms. I also sight-read on the piano, incorporated the vocal line into the accompaniment of a nineteenth-century song at sight, harmonised a given melody, transposed a hymn down a tone and up a half-tone and finally – to my enormous delight as the examination was testing and the room was scorching hot – I had the opportunity of improvising on the title "Anger leading to peace". It just poured out quite naturally and I went out peacefully.

The practical music therapy was assessed by the case notes submitted, by the observations of the training music therapists in the institutions visited (in my case St Lawrence's Hospital for the Severely Subnormal, Caterham, and St Bernard's Hospital, Southall) and by the answers and the manner of their presentation at the viva voce before a panel which, in my year, consisted of a psychiatrist, a composer and a musically oriented teacher of handicapped children. Also at this occasion I had to play three pieces to suggest different moods, from memory on the piano, and defend my choices. I played Bartók's *Sorrow*, Anthony Hopkins' Fourths from *For Talented Beginners* (as anger) and I forget the third. But what I do remember, and I think I will never forget, is the vision of the closed, angry faces of the composer and teacher disputing my choice of anger on the grounds that it contained no discords, and my sudden awareness of the beautiful open and enabling silent receptivity of that psychiatrist. Perhaps this was one of the most valuable lessons of the whole course for me.

The psychology examination was based partly on essays submitted throughout the year to the lecturing clinical psychologist of the London University Extension course which we attended, and partly on the viva voce. Although this course, entitled Introduction to Psychology, was largely about the history of psychology as the science of behaviour, my viva was all on the work of Freud.

I consider that this is a fair and comprehensive examination. One student may be almost inarticulate in the viva through nerves and yet show by his written work and practical therapy that he knows what is necessary. Another musician may be less skilled on his instrument and yet use the little skill that he has well and make up for it in his excellent practical work and observations. A third may be quite unable to string two written sentences together yet be so brilliantly articulate and such a convincing performer that this need not cripple him.

THE DIPLOMA COURSE

At present twelve students are taken on yearly for this course. In my year there were seven full-time students and two part-time. Although there were roughly 23 years between the youngest and eldest members, we were a very united and enthusiastic group. It might be useful here to explain why I, in fact, took my two LGSM exams at once. In one of the early seminars, Juliette Alvin passed round photos of severely subnormal adults and adolescents playing instruments together. I had never seen such people. I was so stunned with horror, thinking that I would never be able to cope with both the patients and my feelings about them that when the seminar was over I ran down to the office of the Guildhall and put my name on a list to take the violin teaching examination as well. The first institution that I was sent to was St Lawrence's Hospital for the Severely Subnormal. Of course, when I got there I found that the children were nothing like the photographs. Physically, yes perhaps, but they laughed and cried, showed fear and anger and often their eyes shone with pure delight at the music. My love for them and curiosity about them banished all fear and distaste. Nobody told me it would be like this. But had they done so I would not today have been a qualified violin teacher.

Each one of us had one hour a week of tuition on our first study instrument and a half hour on the second. One of these had to be the piano. Some of the pianists did not play a second instrument and had hastily to learn to play the guitar, recorder or other relatively quickly learnt instrument; but we all passed somehow.

There were weekly psychology lectures when we joined an existing evening class and monopolised most of the question time. There were weekly lectures by members of related disciplines. Eminent psychiatrists gave lectures on such subjects as "mental health", "the psychotic patient", "the Ten Commandments of a therapist" and "music therapy in a psychiatric hospital". One of them delighted us by saying, "The biggest things [in a psychiatric hospital] I learnt not from doctors and nurses but from the art therapists, music therapist and chaplain." Specialist physicians spoke on "autism", "the handicapped child" and "the cerebral palsied child" among other things. Some of the other lectures were "How to handle groups" by a psychiatric social worker from the Tavistock Clinic, "The music therapist in the team" and "Keeping records" by a music therapist. Our essays were planned to bring the musical and psychological threads together with such titles as "Some musical aspects of my student life", "How improved communication was established with a patient through music", "The musical needs of the five-year-old child", "The maladjusted adult in the normal group", "The maladjusted person in the therapeutic group" and "The characteristics of normal family groups and their effects on children". Tutorials were closely concerned with the effect of music on ourselves. Some of the essay titles were "What music helped me to develop in my personality", "Why I feel as I do about various kinds of playing: orchestral, solo, chamber music etc.", "What is my relationship to my teachers and fellow students through music?" and "Why I took up the study of music".

Great importance was attached to the seminars. Most of a musician's training is either on an intense one to one basis, or else it is in leader-oriented groups such as orchestras and choirs, and in lectures and aural training classes. Apart from the time spent rehearsing chamber music, there is little practice in democratic teamwork. In his work in an institution, the musician needs to turn his extroversion not only towards his musical outlet but also to his verbal exchange with the members of the interdisciplinary team. This can be difficult. Some musicians can only express their deepest and most sincere feelings through music; words are used for trite everyday transactions or abreaction jokes about their conductors. Faced with the solemnity and weight of communication of the average psychiatrist or social worker, this kind of musician is in danger of freezing up completely or playing chameleon and becoming an inadequate cerebral communicator instead of allowing the good qualities of emotional sensitivity and generosity, which his training has developed in him, to shine. So while we threshed out child development and music therapy theories, we also learnt to relate to one another in a group. It is important for students to make the best possible use of these hours, learning both how to speak, and – even more important – how and when to remain silent.

The practical work took place one day weekly, the students acting as trainee music therapists under the guidance of the institution's music therapists. At once this made all those dry theories come alive, and those days became for me the heart of the course. The stories which the other students brought back from their institutions were particularly intriguing. A thalidomide boy with only rudimentary limbs was now taking musical dictation. A geriatric group were giving a little concert. A spastic girl playing the flute was gaining more and more control over her arms, motivated by the wish to play in the orchestra for the handicapped. In this way we all got a glimpse into every kind of music therapy except perhaps private practice.

At 9.30 every Friday morning we all assembled in one of the organ rooms at the Guildhall for keyboard work with our fierce, brilliant and often very entertaining organist teacher. First we thumped our way through our transpositions. (I only managed to pass by transposing a hymn a tone and semi-tone up and down before breakfast every day for a year). Then we frantically pulled the vocal parts of songs into instantly edited versions of the thickets of notes which made up their accompaniments. Next we harmonised violin parts of quartets. And then the fun began. The fun was classical improvisation. Sometimes we had to improvise piano or organ solos in a chosen form or style – a minuet, march or waltz. Sometimes we were given a written harmonic plan of four to sixteen repeated bars, and two of us would sit at the organ, two at the piano and the other three played clarinet, flute and violin, and we all improvised within this harmonic structure. The concordance was a delight. And then one day I was given a wiggly line to look at. "Play that." I did, in the atonal style that we were being taught in the modern improvisation class. The teacher was delighted. He tried other kinds of free stimuli. We responded. I think that was how the free improvisation title crept into the examination.

MODERN IMPROVISATION

This class lasted one and a half hours weekly but I am giving it a section to itself because I, among many others, found it so seminally valuable. The professor was the composer Alfred Nieman. He, himself, had always improvised freely in the atonal manner but had not concerned himself with the idea of taking an improvisation class until approached by some Guildhall students wanting advice about quite another sort of improvisation. He was puzzled that anyone should find this difficult.

Generous in mind and gentle, Nieman was alternately loving, angry, provocative, petulant and inspired but always marvellously creative. We were bound to him in such a fierce love-hate relationship that the first thing we qualified therapists ask a trainee is: "How do you get on with Nieman?" This was the human catalyst.

At the first lesson we were told that we were going to learn to break up all the obsolete and old forms of diatonic, melodic and harmonic structure and move into something much more free, personal and trans-personal. The introductory rules were that we were not to use octaves, or more than three consecutive chromatic steps, or any honest common chords and arpeggios or to play in accordance with any recognisable time signature. What was left?

The answer was sometimes pointillistic music in non-pulse rhythm, sometimes the vast long-lined music of the wind and waves. Previously, I had been used to creating a tonal structure and then filling it with the appropriate emotions according to the composer's dynamic markings, or, when composing, feeling the music alive inside me and writing down the symbols to indicate its structure. But now the emotion itself was to be the force which would instantly claim its own musical form. I was frightened. Supposing it didn't.

The title of my very first improvisation was "Fear". I stood up in front of the class and approached the form-giving instrument. For a while I sat frozen in front of the grand piano, staring at the black and white keys. Inside me were feelings enough, churning away like the wake of an ocean liner. But the gulf between the inner and the outer was vast. A chasm. Just to connect the two stretched my mind almost to breaking point.

At last I plunged in, feeling that it was immeasurably dangerous to unleash these painful feelings of terror on the world. Plonk! Rumble, rumble, tinkle, plonk! Wow! But it was great! I liked it. I felt power. I felt affirmation of being. I no longer was in the grip of this emotion but could use it. Create with it. It was fun. A marvellous game.

It would have been nice to be able to report that my first brave instant creation was the staggering success I felt it to be. Of course, it wasn't. It was even criticised as being "too tame" and "too conventional". At least I had damaged no one. I had had visions of several people fainting and the rest flying in panic from the room. They all sat solidly in their seats. Anyhow, I was initiated. An invisible thread of sound now led from the inner world to the outer. In the months that followed we learned to respond to one another sensitively through sound, spinning strange webs of intricate poly-phonic, arhythmic, atonal patterns which were recorded, evaluated by each one of us and pulled ruthlessly to pieces over and over again. Creation and destruction. Anabolism and katabolism. We were at one with the processes of life itself. There follow some impressions of what attendance at this class meant to one student – a mature student – who had never improvised a note in her life. It was a mysterious awakening.

You itch on the piano instead of holding back
Alfred Nieman wanted us to hold back until moved to make music by a genuine impulse. "You can't stop to think if this is the note you intended," he said, "A rhythmic impulse will take hold of you, you will explore this in terms of a more spacious line which will move out in wider circles." What he called "The feeling of music inside you leading you on" was a recognisable and exciting experi-ence giving great joy and freedom. Somehow it reminded me of the experience of people who told me that they spoke in tongues.

Improvising chamber music is pouncing on an opportunity
We communicated in tones and lines and phrases. "Just a gesture – it opens up doors at once," he said. I went through miseries of inadequacy. "Conceive a line. Give birth to it. You can't just wait for someone to feed you." We learnt to fill empty spaces and come to meet each other's ideas. "You mustn't ask for everything to be favourable to you, you have got to step in and make it favourable." This was one of Nieman's most resonating phrases which has carried over into areas far beyond the piano, drums, xylophone, glocken-spiel, flute, clarinet and violin.

Don't think of ideas beforehand, you must learn to trust your intuition
This way of playing affected my whole life. Others said the same. "You have got to get into this world where things happen. You don't know how they happen but they do." When I thought the impulse had seized me he roared at me for sounding like an old rabbi – I had just been studying some Bloch. "Trust the moment. It is pregnant, it will give birth." On the other hand we were to be absolutely in control. "Don't get carried away by the emotion that you are trying to express; you must stand outside it." How necessary this is when one is playing with an excited patient who is so far from standing outside her own furious drumming experience.

This breaking up of the 1, 2, 3 is exciting. Rhythm is the key to the inner world

He told us to go home and explore this field. "The atonal way is the quickest, the most secret way." I took to improvising for ten minutes on the piano every morning to gain freedom, sometimes playing incidents from my dreams or ideas from my analytical psychotherapy sessions. I found that this inchoate music was, for me, a vital link between structured music and the music of life. I would sit in the train listening intently to the sounds of the engine and the closing doors. I would turn to sound the rhythm of the wind sweeping up a pile of leaves and throwing them into the air. Or translate a bird's flight into the sustained tones of a violin or wind instrument. I found a greater capacity for quiet delight, awe and wonder in the music of everyday life.

Various techniques explored

We improvised duets on the piano. I played treble to Nieman's bass. It was the most intimate experience I have ever had with anyone – excluding infant feeding and sex. The shock of the instant responses. The sudden onenesses. The teetering crescendo to the climax. His springing like a scalded cat to shattering dissonances when I accidentally fell on an honest C major triad. I felt that it was I that was the therapist, containing all his emotion, not the reverse.

After a long period of experiments with chamber music groups of three or four players – marvellous training in analysing subverbal group expression for the observers – we tried symphonies where one conductor unleashed musical forces and controlled the sound dynamics. As a player it was exhilarating and satisfying. However, as the conductor I soon felt like the Sorcerer's Apprentice. I dropped the baton and fled to my seat in the middle.

We played Responses, starting with a phrase or a held note. "These sounds are yours and they are very important. Keep them as long as you like," said Nieman. It was a permission to launch out serenely through the fourth dimension. The free form was difficult to follow at first. Gradually it began to mean something. "In chamber music you must give as well as receive. There is nothing more wonderful than being able to share. Whether it's your spirit of perversity or reluctance. Never mind. There is a feeling of acceptance of being made into a group pattern, however odd or inadequate the individual contributions are, they all make one strong whole." But my notes that day were disenchanted. I wrote, "All tense, nervous, sensitive and deeply inhibited and joyless." It was not an effortless development.

Sometimes we improvised concertos, all the instruments reflecting and holding the soloist but letting her shine. Once we had an abstract mime stimulus created by two students moving strange objects like a paper flower, a doll, a cup, a candle, a cube, a pair of spectacles and so on, with all the others responding with instant music. It was splendid practice for reacting to patients' music. This kind of exercise increased our creativity and spontaneity in life as well as in music.

You are privileged people . . .
Nieman would suddenly launch out into the most pregnant phrases. One day he said, "Music faces us with the realisation that there are two worlds: the inner and the outer. The inner is often incommunicable, a spiritual world which is difficult to enter from the outer world where we normally speak to one another. Music is a bridge for us by which we can reach this inner world. That is why this free expression is so vital for music therapy. You are privileged people to be able to communicate with this deepest part of human beings." Little did we realise at that time just how significant this communication was going to be and what value it could have in helping to change the direction of ruined lives.

3. Analytical music therapy and Intertherap

Analytical music therapy is a way of exploring the unconscious with an analytical music therapist by means of sound expression. It is a way of getting to know oneself, possibly as a greater self than one had realised existed. It may be very painful to admit the existence of some parts of it and to realise that they were once all that one hated or envied most cruelly in others. It may be very frightening to accept the challenge of other parts. Analytical music therapy is also a way of synthesising the energies freed from repressive and defensive mechanisms and giving them a new direction through rehearsal of action in sound. The term "analytical music therapy" was first used by Peter Wright, music therapist, to describe the particular work that we were engaged in and experimenting with at that time.*

The purpose of analytical music therapy is to free the maximum amount of energy for use in the achievement of the client's greater life aim. This may include releasing energy bound up in the repressing of images or memories in the unconscious because of the fear of their disturbing emotional content. It may include revealing energy sources trapped into the patterns of destructive games or physical symptoms, or intensely dynamic hopes kept frozen solid by fear.

To the client, the purpose may be to rid herself of some unwanted symptom, neatly and surgically without disturbing the balance elsewhere. But working with the psyche is like a game of spillikins, everything depends on everything else, and a new balance must be evolved to make the new freedom workable and tenable.

PREPARATION

When the musician has passed his LGSM (Music Therapy) he is a qualified music therapist but he is not yet ready to practise as an analytical music therapist. For this, a further period, not so much of study but of a special kind of interpersonal and intrapersonal experience, is needed. First of all he will be greatly helped by having some sessions with a psychoanalyst or analytical psychotherapist in

* See Vol. 3 No. 2 of the *British Journal of Music Therapy*.

order to explore and come to terms with his own unconscious and the way its crippling protective mechanisms, unsuspected hidden instinctive urges and unrealised highest life drives are producing warping stress in his own life. If he does not do this, or at very least work with some case supervision by an analytical psychotherapist or analytical music therapist, although no one can prevent him from using the analytical music therapy techniques described later on in this book, he may possibly find that in using them his own problems will become interlocked with those of his client. Then at best the progress of the treatment will come to a bewildering halt; and at worst both of them will get into grave danger through becoming a double channel for unconscious forces, which he can neither understand nor control because of his lack of experience and guidance.

Perhaps I should make that less terrifying by saying that any couple – colleagues, flat-mates, lovers or marriage partners – who experience life intensely together lay themselves open to this kind of danger. In the case of a church marriage, this is done after the promise to love and cherish the partner whatever turn events may take. The pair have some hint that this may be an effort. But with other two-person relationships one promises nothing and all hell may be let loose. It can be quite baffling. But the therapist is selling his capacity for healing and caring. He should at least endeavour to know what he is about and be aware of the dangers en route. He cannot be perfect (and no amount of analysis will remove every weakness and blindspot) but at least he can do his best to prepare himself for the work responsibly. So much he owes to himself, the client and the work.

Analysis or analytical psychotherapy caters for one part of the work but in order to practise analytical music therapy it is necessary for the musician to know how to translate this work and these mental concepts and verbal realisations into emotional sound expression. He must know this experience from the inside – from the client's side – and understand the full force of its depth and power and physical realisation. For this he needs a period of Intertherap, regular weekly music therapy workshop meetings – preferably during the period of his own analysis or analytical psychotherapy where he can gain experience with other music therapists both in working through his own problems as an analytical music therapist and in developing his own capacity and techniques as therapist to another therapist undergoing the client experience. There is no pretending in the Intertherap sessions. Real problems are always dealt with and because of the depth-dredging of the parallel analysis or analytical psychotherapy they are often very disturbing. Thus new techniques are always discussed and developed and experienced from both sides in the Intertherap before being taken out into the open therapeutic field. With his first client outside the Intertherap the analytical music therapist does not feel like a novice. The training has given him both understanding and empathy with the client and experience in holding the emotion as a therapist.

Analytical music therapy in action
To the therapist, an important part of analytical music therapy is the re-polarisation of the patient's creativity, turning it from negative to positive use. A psychiatric patient, for example, may be using her creativity in life to act out the frustration caused by her intruding mother through refusing food, taking overdoses, maintaining self-destructive and denigrating relationships. All this takes vital creative energy. When the music therapist can persuade her to act out some of these communications in sound, immediately the creativity becomes a positive use of energy. It is an act of generosity and trust, bridging the inner world of frustration and hate with the sound expression in the outer world which is accepted with understanding and possibly enthusiasm by the therapist. New possibilities for more creative expression and communication can be gradually realised.

The analytical music therapist is greatly helped by music in his work with resistances and the transference. The transference, within which the client acts out her feelings towards an earlier loved or hated person, occurs because the memory of the original situation and feelings is too painful to recall. Energy is used in blocking the memory and forcing the client to behave "as if" in the original situation. The resistances here are to the feelings concerned with the memory because of the fear of "going mad" or being utterly unable to contain them. As an example: a middle-aged, divorced woman client, Mrs S., was finding herself impossibly aggressive to a new member of the firm where she worked. This colleague, a Miss B., was younger, more attractive, very much like the client's husband's second wife and she was receiving a great deal of attention from her next-in-command Mr E. whom Mrs S. both loved and admired. During her session, Mrs S., on drums and cymbal, thundered out her rage and distress at being so slighted by Mr E. and at the end of this found that this turmoil was the cover for a feeling of deep, deep sadness. Together with the therapist in music she went into the sound of this sadness and suddenly had an inner image of herself in a cot and her father saying goodnight and leaving the room with her mother dressed in a fur coat. The feeling of being so uselessly small and impotent in the cot and the longing to be with him was overwhelming but the music contained the emotion and allowed the emergence of this image. This experience was the keynote of her jealousy at work. The knowledge of this took the time resonances* slowly from the work situation. Mrs S. gradually felt that she was no longer little and impotent, nor was Mr E. her beloved father but in fact the dutiful husband of a contented Mrs E. She began to use her creativity to form the image of the kind of satisfactory real relationship that she would like to have with a man of her own.

An important feature of music is its existence in the dimension of time. This enables an emotional experience to undergo the process of what Jung termed enantiodromia (something turning into its opposite, i.e. love to hate). It offers tremendous freedom and confidence in the goodness of life to be able to give full vent to one's hate through an acceptable musical channel and find that after a time of mounting, incredibly savage fury and destructive emotion and cacophony, nothing is destroyed, nothing is spoiled around one, but that one is wonderfully changed and liberated inside and where there was only darkness and distress there is now light, vibration and courage. That is experiencing enantiodromia. This is the experience Jung valued so highly, saying, "Real liberation comes not from glossing over or repressing painful states of feeling but only from experiencing them to the full."

INTERTHERAP

Music therapy is not just a treatment for "them": the handicapped, the sick, the deranged, hallucinated, depressed, elated, deluded and emotionally wounded. It is a way for anyone who can make use of it. As such it must be a way that is known by those guiding others. Hence the need for Intertherap. These analytical music therapy training groups should contain from three to five music therapists each of whom must have a chance to be both therapist and client. The therapist/client relationships should remain stable within the group so that the therapist has time to build up a memory bank of the client's images, dreams, colour symbolism, rhythmic development and so on, and to see the route along which the work is developing.

* For explanation see p. 134.

Preparation

The work must be taken seriously, for the means are most powerful and the experiment is with his colleague's valuable mental and emotional life. It is not helpful to have observers in the Intertherap, partly because the process should be viewed on the basis of a long-term development, partly because the material which emerges is often extremely confidential and partly because the client's emotional responses can be so strong that he might feel embarrassed to be seen weeping, snarling or screaming with delight over his instrument by people who have not, themselves, had similar experiences. Then his subsequent inhibition would detract from the value of the work. Each member should have at least 45 minutes' therapy and there should be time for discussion and any experiments which members wish to try out.

Although no analytical music therapist can consider his training complete without a period of Intertherap, it is possible for a music therapist to take part in Intertherap even though he is not in analysis or having analytical psychotherapy. It means that as therapist he may choose to work more on the surface and use only such techniques as he feels capable of handling. His own therapist in the Intertherap sessions should be an analytical music therapist.

A weekly Intertherap session is recommended, if possible held as soon after members' analytical sessions as can be conveniently arranged. It seems almost the rule to emerge from an analytical psychotherapy session in a state of emotional turmoil, though with valuable insights, and this lasts for up to four days ordinarily. Intertherap sessions tend to leave the members physically relaxed with a feeling of having created a viable sound structured response to life, even though the matters worked through may have been extremely disturbing. It is the absence of doing which makes psychotherapy so frustrating; it is the experience of sound creation using the whole emotional spectrum, the intuition in the music, plus the reciprocal humanity of the members, which make Intertherap a satisfying experience.

Intertherap impressions

(The session material is not really typical, having been carefully chosen from my notebooks to exclude material too private for this kind of publication or quite incomprehensible due to its being a part of a dream series or a train of events which would take too long to relate.)

It is evening. For a week I have been gathering disturbing events,

36

emotions and dreams like a harassed shopper. Now I have come home to open the parcels. With me are Marjorie and Peter, both music therapists and pianists. Marjorie is not in analysis at present. It is my turn to be the client. This week I have the imminent prospect of becoming a mother-in-law. Marjorie sits at the piano. "I would like to play mother-in-law," I say. I sit on the windowseat with the tom-tom and cymbal to the right, xylophone in front, gong to the left and Chinese temple bell, Swiss cow bell and triangle hanging from a music stand behind. With drumtaps and cymbal I start out being the classical irritable and interfering mother-in-law. The music takes me further inside. Marjorie's piano music is holding the outer boundaries. I lose time/space awareness. I am by the seashore somewhere unknown and peaceful. I create it but it creates me, too. I feel that my busy procreative phase is over. The sounds are gentle and mysterious like the sea withdrawing on a beach of tiny, shining pebbles. I play the gong gently and listen to it deeply and quietly reverberating. Now I can live more for values, peaceful and withdrawn. I stop and sigh. I tell Marjorie what I saw. "It will be a creative thing not a role thrust upon me by one thousand and one variety artists." I will write to Karen tomorrow. I will go to meet it.

Marjorie's approach is reassuringly client-centred. I find that her music brings up the thoughts and feelings. The words I want to work out for myself.

At this time I am on the Introductory course of the Institute for Group Analysis. After the weekly lecture and discussion I am one of one of the many groups of fourteen psychiatrists, doctors, nurses, psychologists and psychiatric social workers who sit in circles talking while a group-analyst analyses the proceedings. Frankly I am hating every minute of it. "There is something which I cannot decide whether or not to tell that group," I say. "Could we improvise Telling the Group?" "Do you want a holding?" Marjorie asks. "No, thanks, I'd rather be me and have you be all of them. I don't find them particularly pleasant."

Yes, I'll tell them on the drum. I start off. Tap, tap, tap, bang, thud, thump. Telling them? I'm just simply killing them. Beating the living daylights out of them. If I experience them as unpleasant it is surely mutual. Every time I hear a peep out of the piano I smash it dead on the cymbal or drum. I am enjoying it immensely. I feel I have the whole situation really under control. Then suddenly the drumstick slips on to the rounded centre of the cymbal with a clear, dry, sophisticated sound. I like it. I do it again. And again. I hear the piano but it doesn't threaten me now. I can tell the group or I can NOT tell them. I am free. My expression can be willed and creative and elegant. It need not be like exploding or wetting my pants but controlled with as much or as little emphasis as the moment requires. I stop and tell Marjorie. She tells me the feelings she got while I played. It is all right. The whole situation seems more manageable.

"I would like to explore a strange experience which has haunted me for five days. It was as if the past were rolled up so there was no memory and the future rolled up so there was no anxiety or desire and nothing existed except in the present and I imagined this present as being held in the hand of God. It was quite extraordinarily peaceful. Like a moment of eternity." Bells and chimebars and xylophone glissandi with the piano interwoven made the majesty of God and the glory of the heaven world. The gong and cymbal brought it down to me in the present, just being, peacefully, with music as the enclosing holding of the hand of God. We made a gentle, ebbing decrescendo and stopped. "What did you discover?" asked Marjorie. "It didn't add anything to the peaceful feeling but all that joy, which I didn't feel before, was all wrapped up in it. It is not the sort of thing that one can ordinarily speak about. It was reassuring to try to share it. I don't feel so lonely with it. But it is very real to me. Just as real as eating a poached egg or cleaning my violin. Perhaps more."

"Any dreams?" asked Marjorie. "I've got one horror but I think I will keep it for my psychotherapist first," I answer. "Anything left over from your psychotherapy?" she asks. "Only a bottomless pit of fury," I answer. "Would you like me to be him?" "No, I would like you to help me to contain my feelings," I say and turn to the instrument. It was the drum, the three-legged tom-tom, that took the first beating. When the sticks are held very flat, a terrible dead boom of sound roars out. I launched into the emotion and leaned on the sound. It carried me. More anger than I knew existed in the world welled up and out and exploded into decibels without form, without boundary, without the limits imposed by any kind of rhythmic order. I hacked him to pieces and crushed him into powder for the searing pain that he had caused me. There was a moment of panic that the emotion would break right out of my mind. I threw more into the music, which miraculously held it. Too much anger even for the drum. I turned to the cymbal and cascades of violence and fury crashed down on the golden disc which trembled with dazzling vibrations. Suddenly something seemed to jerk down inside me and it was all different. In my inner imagery I had shrunk to mid-calf height and was happily jogging down a jungle trail behind the giant figure of my psychotherapist, I drummed rhythmically mezzo forte to our footsteps in a mood of contented expectancy. Every now and then he would stop and point to something on the trail. Bang! Crash! The rhythm balked and the piano answered. Crack! I grew to his height. We fought. This time the hostility came from both sides. No longer mindless waterfalls of fury but thought, action, cunning and wicked speed quicker than a snake's tongue. Sounds on bells and drums and cymbals interspersed with piano tone clusters. I stopped. It was good. No one had to be killed or to kill. It wasn't like that this time. It was being whole and using the fury and accepting the other's right to do the same. Fighting to live and surviving the use of aggression. My body hummed in the arms and trunk. Then down into the feet. I felt fine. Mind had entered this emotional field like a portcullis guarding a gateway. "Thanks, Marjorie," I said, coming to outer awareness again, "I suppose I'll survive next week, too."

I find that this basic image of anger as being all-obliterating, from one side or the other, often prevents my clients from being able freely to express even such firmness as is justified and necessary in dealing with their family, pupils or colleagues. If they take one aggressive move, they say, they will simply be unable to control themselves and someone will be killed or kill. The result is that their anger turns to trembling, tears or psychosomatic disorders.

My session being over, I write up my notes with half an ear open to Peter taking Marjorie's session. Their music is very sensitive and beautiful. She is not yet into the murderous stage. I will not describe their sessions because that is their private experience and they may need it to be part of some other book. I will only say that when it is my turn to be Peter's analytical music therapist, the miserable angry child client self of my therapy vanishes. As I sit at the piano I am strong and somehow larger than myself. Do I become the giant I was following down the trail? I don't know. I only know that again and again I realise that it is the client who creates the therapist through his trust and his needs.

4. Choosing the field of action

Having trained and qualified, the musician is now ready to become a therapist. The Diploma doesn't give him this different state of being. No amount of learning or examinations will do this for him. Only one thing – his clients with their trust and their needs. This is what draws that different quality of being into a therapist and changes his life and attitudes. It doesn't happen all at once. The first time a child comes to him locked in its world of mute dreams he can have spasms of helplessness. The first few times that a client pours out her distress and her intimate problems to him can make him feel very inadequate. But the client's trust and belief in the therapist's role seems to strengthen his therapeutic orientation like the sunshine strengthening the newly emerged butterfly's wings; suddenly he can stretch out those wings and use them. The client seldom realises what a creative part she plays.

I never had to choose my field of action. It chose me. As soon as I started my practical training in the psychiatric hospital I knew that this was what I wanted to do. It was the emotional pain that drew me. Here was something to work with, a kind of fuel which could be used to give a new direction to a life. Perhaps it sounds sinister but I felt that this was a sensitivity that I could use. Curiously enough, in my training year each one of the trainee therapists felt naturally drawn to one or other kind of patient. There was no category that no one liked, and this was reassuring. I think that music therapy is vocational. It is taxing work and therefore it is necessary for the therapist to find his own particular satisfactions in doing it if he is going to be able to continue to carry on year in and year out.

Should one start full-time as a therapist or part-time? Most music therapists like to keep a foot in the normal everyday world and spend part of their time teaching or playing (although it can be difficult to fit in rehearsals on the free days). In this way they find that one job complements the other and they keep fresh for both. Basically the music therapist is still a musician. He needs to play music for its own sake, to study it, perfom it and enjoy it. Somewhere, even if only in one corner of his life, music must be allowed to have first place, to stretch him, to replenish him and to bring him into contact with his fellow musicians. Where his work leaves no place for this, something begins to wither.

If he does decide to practise full-time as a therapist, there is the question of whether to work in one place – and this is most likely to be a hospital – or to divide his time between different kinds of work. The latter is possibly more stimulating but it can be tiring to adjust to the different settings. On the other hand settling down in one institution can narrow his viewpoint and smother him in inter-team intrigues. However, there is also the possibility of forming a really rich and interacting team relationship and going deeply into the possibilities and problems posed by the particular work.

Some thought should be given to whether the music therapist wants to work where he is the only one of his kind or if he would enjoy being in a larger Music Therapy Department. It is my experience that it is a great source of enrichment, relaxation and humour to be with other musicians. Those who play melodic instruments can perform in hospital wards with the pianists. This improves the all-round quality of music performed as most institutional pianos are geriatric, below pitch and sadly ailing. Movement groups are very much easier where one therapist can lead the movement and the other provide the music. However, as this is a pioneer profession most therapists start on their own in a hospital, special school, day centre or special unit where there has never been a music therapist before and they have to build up from there.

The chances of seeing the job he wants advertised in a professional magazine or national newspaper are slight. As a rule the music therapist must himself create the job, seeing the possibilities of his work helping a certain group of handicapped individuals and suggesting to the authorities that he be taken on. Sometimes the authorities themselves hear about music therapy and apply to the British Society for Music Therapy for the name of a qualified music therapist.

Here are some notes on various categories of people who can benefit from music therapy. If the therapist has not had experience with a certain category during his training then I recommend going to see them, discussing the various problems and possible difficulties with the staff and borrowing the equipment to try a few experimental sessions to see how he feels with the group and how they respond to him. The clients for individual music therapy in private practice are discussed elsewhere.

EDUCATIONALLY SUBNORMAL CHILDREN

The restlessness and constant activity of these children makes work in large groups extremely difficult. This is a group which badly needs success. Sometimes their subnormality is not lack of innate intelligence as much as a deprived family background and impoverished emotional life. Where possible something should be created round the abilities of each child, however modest, to make him feel that his particular talents are appreciated by the group and the therapist. Simple instruments such as drums, clappers, one-string fiddles, maraccas and claves can be made. Songs sung to instruments and piano. Very small improvisation groups can communicate instrumentally and as accompaniment to hand ballets or mimed scenes. A responsive, creative approach with a warm and encouraging personality is necessary for the therapist.

THE SEVERELY SUBNORMAL

Even the most severely handicapped individuals often respond to the stimulus of sound with movement or a look of pleasure in the eyes. Portable instruments are useful for taking into wards where immobile patients sit or lie. Even aphasic (dumb) children have been taught to move in time to different note values picking out a wooden cut-out musical symbol and carrying it round with appropriate steps when their note value is played. Their sense of achievement is touching. Bands of drum and harmonica players can accompany the pianist, learning control, sensitivity and social sense. Rhythm they have little trouble in learning. Improvisation groups have trained their sensitivity and alertness with some beautiful musical results using drums, tambour, tambourine, melodica, guitar, glockenspiel, xylophone, bells and maraccas with the therapist directing from the piano. Simple plays can be enacted with musical phrases guiding the stage movements. The individual child is stimulated through the curiosity drive by exploring different sounds and tactile sensations on various instruments with the therapist. Music is an important expressive communication for the aphasic child, it really opens up some children and seems to produce a feeling of awe, wonder and delight. Indomitable perseverance and love of the child nature are needed for this work.

THE PHYSICALLY HANDICAPPED

Physically handicapped children need special help in being able to accept themselves as they are and if they can do this it is a great deal easier for them to be accepted by others. Movement through time with music helps the physically handicapped person to tolerate the lack of movement through space. Long hours immobile on their own makes music a useful hobby offering scope for self-expression, creativity and the possibility of giving pleasure to others. There are instruments to cater for a great variety of handicaps. Even a person who can only move his head and jaw can play a transistorised stylophone. The pianist without legs can use a specially invented pedalling device. A one-armed string player can sometimes bow with her artificial arm. Breathing is often poor in these people but improves markedly as they strive to learn to phrase musically on a melodica, recorder or, perhaps later, on one of the orchestral wind instruments. Singing can be a great joy and the possibility of joining a choir broadens avenues of communication. Spastics are very much helped by the relaxation induced by gentle music which eases their movements. Through learning to play instruments many are motivated to perform movements which they had formerly found impossible. Music can also play a similar part in retraining stroke victims. In a band, even athetoid spastics (having a compulsive writhing movement) can put these movements to good use in playing bells or maraccas. The therapist needs plenty of ingenuity and enthusiasm.

MALADJUSTED CHILDREN

These children are often very bright but usually have a short concentration span. Music can help them to find an acceptable outlet for their turbulent emotions and through improvisation they themselves can learn to create a structure to hold these emotions. Singing, learning instruments and reading and writing music bring a sense of achievement and satisfaction. The therapist needs quick wits, stability, warmth and a high toleration of chaos.

PSYCHIATRIC PATIENTS

I have described this work in detail elsewhere in this book. The changing emotional state of the short-stay patients demands an extra-sensitive and adaptable response from the therapist who also needs the capacity to be able to accept rejection and acute emotional distress in others, coupled with a firm anchor in his private life.

THE BLIND

Contrary to popular opinion not all blind people are musical. For those that are, richness of musical texture with varied timbre and rich harmonies can do something to compensate for lack of visual light and colour. Instruments which require sensitive touch are recommended to develop this faculty. Singing at once in parts makes this a more exciting and challenging experience for the blind group. Improvisation groups help to replace isolation with sensitive distance communication. Expressive movement to music increases the blind person's trust of the environment and combats the usual rather withdrawn, careful posture. The therapist needs an imaginative auditory and tactile approach.

AUTISTIC CHILDREN

Even the most withdrawn aphasic child can benefit from total response music therapy where her every move is taken as a communication and responded to musically by the therapist. With this technique the therapist can react more sensitively with a xylophone, string or wind instrument where he can face the child, see every slightest movement and catch every attempt at communication. Some of these children tolerate sung communication before spoken. With music they also usefully sing about emotions which they are not yet ready to tolerate as direct experiences. Work usually starts with the individual child, building up a relationship using musical improvisation on percussion, cymbals and possibly a xylophone with the therapist on the piano and singing. Later the child can enter a group and learn more organised songs and pieces. The therapist needs great sensitivity and a high toleration of rejection.

SUPERGIFTED CHILDREN

These children are more unusual, statistically, than the severely subnormal. Their high intelligence can bring communication problems with their contemporaries which may mean that they miss out, emotionally, on a number of vitally important abreactive play experiences and become lopsided in development, favouring intellectual ability at the expense of emotional depth, sensory awareness and intuition. Individual sessions can be planned as therapeutically slanted instrumental tuition or creative sound play sessions, but the quality of the relationship is the vital factor. The therapist needs high intelligence, warmth and a very receptive approach.

Choosing the field of action

GERIATRICS

Remarkable enlivenment can occur in old people as songs from their youth are played and memories stirred, but it is important that the therapist should have time to listen and care. Expressive rhythmic exercises to music, working through the whole body (if necessary sitting down) are helpful. A rhythm session with percussion instruments helps to move stiffening limbs and tone up circulation. Old people are often surprisingly keen to try new musical experiences. One old man in his nineties took up the violin with great pleasure. The therapist needs patience and gentleness.

PRISONERS

Work is just beginning with this group. Music is a happy way of integrating with the social life of the world outside and a great solace to many prisoners. Bands and choirs are already part of the life of some prisons. Small communication and improvisation or psycho-dynamic movement and relaxation groups could possibly help individuals to recover some of the spontaneity and creativity lost in the institutionalised life pattern. The therapist needs firmness, stability and the ability to communicate easily with all kinds of people.

5. Repertoire and instruments

The musical repertoire required by the therapist will, of course, depend on what kind of patients he is treating and under what circumstances. What I wish to avoid, in speaking about repertoire, is to set myself up as the ultimate authority on the subject, then giving any kind of official list of desirable pieces of music. This would be damaging if it prevented even one future music therapist from doing his own invaluable original thinking and exploration in this important aspect of the work.

SOLO REPERTOIRE

The therapist may need a number of short pieces to play at the end of his individual sessions to bring the client back, by means of the structured music, to externally directed consciousness. He will certainly also need music to play on the words and in concerts in hospitals. If he aims for a minimum of seventeen slow and the same number of faster pieces, playing one of each once weekly he will only repeat himself three times a year. This will hardly be too much for either the patients, the staff or himself.

What kind of music is suitable? If one is ill – especially mentally ill – one needs music which speaks to one's condition. Almost any music which expresses deep feelings is welcomed. Pieces and single movements are preferable to lengthy sonatas, concertos or tone poems. Music which is merely witty, clever or designed to exhibit empty virtuosity, is out of place, except for the odd little firework which can be shot off to show that the therapist has enough respect for his calling to keep his skills polished. Moreover, apart from the patients' point of view, it is extremely difficult for the therapist to give his entire attention to his playing. His audience (for whom he is responsible as there are not always other staff on the ward) may be getting up and pushing the stand over on their way to the lavatory, having seizures, breaking windows, quarrelling, setting their hair alight, or even just appearing to be about to perpetrate any such calamities as may have occurred during his previous sessions.

I reckon that ward circumstances cut down the therapist's potential technique by about 20 per cent; so that if he has not got this to spare in a difficult piece, he would be well advised to drop it.

The music therapist will need a solo repertoire which covers the whole range of human emotions. It is possible that his present collection has been built up unconsciously excluding one or other emotion which is vitally necessary for a complete approach to the emotional resonance of a group or individual. Guilt, for example, is a vital emotion which is often left out but admirably catered for in the work of a composer such as Ernest Bloch. When playing as a therapist, the musician must, more than usual, delve into the depths of himself to find the inner meaning of the music, so that not just his playing but his whole being resonates with this emotion.

What about jazz and pop music? This is amply catered for on the Radio One programmes heard all day on most wards. Patients will often ask the therapist to play a particular piece of music which has special emotional associations for them. It can be useful to purchase, learn and play it. However, he need not feel compelled to be client-centred to the point of feeling that he is prostituting his art. If playing the desired music is repugnant to him, he can say frankly that he does not play that sort of music but that perhaps the patient could sing it for him instead and tell him what she feels about it. There is no need to reject the patient along with the music.

In search of a rich and varied repertoire, each therapist can be a lifelong explorer. He can scour publishers' lists for suitable items, stop at any likely music shop that he passes, note the names of possible pieces or composers heard on the radio and at concerts and contact his fellow music therapists (whose names are on a list sold by the British Society for Music Therapy) who will be only too willing to help him. It is exciting to include a few works by contemporary composers too, and it helps to overcome the feeling that these patients are stuck in some muddy backwater, out of the refreshing mainstream of life. As a violinist, I have been privileged to have had some music specially written for violinist and pianist to play with people of limited performing skill (on chime bars) but plenty of musical enjoyment by Sir Arthur Bliss, Michael Head, Frank Spedding, Alfred Nieman, Humphrey Searle, Peter Wright, Dr Gordon Jacob, Alan Bush, and promises of contributions by Lennox Berkeley, Adrian Crufts, Priaulx Rainer, R. Sherlaw Johnson, John Joubert, Jeremy Dale Roberts, Karlheinz Stockhausen and others. It is a wonderful and encouraging thought that such busy and talented artists of our age have spared the time and thought to let their creations liven up this otherwise forgotten corner of the community. To me it represents a human and emotional level equivalent of the exploration of the dark side of the moon. To the patients it is a joy and delight.

GENERAL REPERTOIRE

On the wards, the therapist will need a basic repertoire of old-time favourites and variety songs which elderly people will remember and respond to when they will respond to little else. These often bring a host of memories which the therapist can use to stimulate conversation. A collection of marches with well known tunes is useful for the percussion work. Very often old people's voices are too frail to make singing a wholly adequate means of expression. It is not a way in which they can fight back at life. But with their arthritic hands, the exercise gained during the percussion marches can also be a valuable outlet for aggressive feelings as well as being good for their circulation.

In most wards there are one or two foreigners, often even more cut off than the others by their failing memories losing the present knowledge of English and reverting to their former native tongue. A book of folk songs from all over the world is extremely valuable. I remember one Polish lady sitting dejectedly in her geriatric chair (like a child's high chair). We showed her Polish folk songs and her eyes shone and she rattled away in Polish and sang at the top of her voice when the piano played with her. At once she was alive and whole and vigorous. The healthy past was with her. The change was most striking.

Hymns were often the first Sunday school songs learnt by children of the nineteenth century and so when they remember nothing else and their eyes cannot focus on print, they can sometimes sing verse after verse of an old hymn with determination and enjoyment. Standing, touched, by one such little old lady, I leaned nearer to her to hear her singing, "Send the bloody bastard home, He's drunk again tonight!" So she evidently remembered her brother's version, too.

In the music therapy room

If this room is also used as a practice room when the therapists are away, it is useful to provide a supply of light and classical piano music from beginner tutors to Beethoven and Mozart sonatas and

Chopin preludes. It is a real solace to short-stay patients to be on their own for a while and to play to themselves or their friends. Plenty of simple duets are useful, too. Some popular songs in easy versions will be appreciated as well as ballads, Gilbert and Sullivan, Schumann, Schubert, Brahms and mixed song collections. This repertoire will develop according to the need and taste of both patients and therapists.

RECORDS

Records will be needed for ward record sessions, individual sessions for listening with the therapist and discussion of material projected on to the music, and for movement and relaxation sessions. For the first two kinds of session, patients may bring their own records; this is to be both welcomed and encouraged. The music of a patient's record may represent a hidden side of herself which, when received by the therapist, is experienced as if this part of herself were being received in reality. A private patient of mine brought along a jazz violin record which I spotted and asked to hear. From his gleeful reaction and the way he secretly and earnestly scrutinised me for my reactions, it was clear that this music represented a very exciting, possibly sexual, part of himself. This music being received with pleasure, he later brought along some similar sheet music for us to play together. His excitement was so intense that it completely ruined his violin tone which became harsh and metallic. At the same time he began to speak about finding himself a girl to go out with, perhaps even a wife. It was as if he felt that if the therapist could safely accept the music of his disturbing feelings and survive, then perhaps it would be safe to share them in reality with another lady.

The recorded repertoire is endless. But the therapist could start by making various musical headings under which he could collect records. They might include:

RHYTHMIC MUSIC: Scottish dances, Latin-American music and Greek folk music.

RELAXING MUSIC: Mozart's *Clarinet Concerto* and *Quintet in A*, Delius' *On Hearing the First Cuckoo in Spring*, Samuel Barber's *Adagio for Strings*.

EVOCATIVE MUSIC: Stravinsky's *The Rite of Spring*, Sibelius' *Violin Concerto in F*, Debussy's *String Quartet in G Minor*, and the most advanced works of Stockhausen, John Cage, Ligeti, Busotti and Dallapiccola.

REASSURING MUSIC: Vivaldi's *The Four Seasons*, Mozart's *Violin Concertos in A and D Major*, Johann Strauss's Waltzes.

MOODS: (Anger) Bartók's *String Quartet No. 5*; (Sadness) Brahms' *Clarinet Quintet in B Minor*; (Guilt) Ernest Bloch's *Schelomo for Cello and Orchestra*; (Love) Wagner's *Liebestod*.

EXOTIC MUSIC: Some classical Indian music for sitar and tablas.

If there is a local immigrant population then it is worth acquiring some music from their country. Otherwise the therapist can borrow the native music of the occasional foreign short-stay patient from his record library. Faced with a psychotic youth from Thailand in my record session, I went to the embassy one evening and gratefully borrowed four Thai records. Their effect on the young man was remarkable; he came out of his bewilderment, really listened to the Thai songs and was then able to continue having a long conversation in broken English with me throughout the rest of the session of Western music. That this was unusual was proved by the fact that I overheard one patient saying to the other, "Why is it that she can talk to him and understand him and none of the nurses?" Music can have a mysterious effect on those who listen to it together. I had accepted his music, he was ready to hear mine.

INSTRUMENTS

Almost all music therapists play the piano and at least one other instrument. What instrument should a piano student, contemplating taking up music therapy, learn as his second study? I think that if I were not a violinist and in love with its repertoire and superb and challenging sensitivity, then I would learn to sing and play the guitar or flute. The guitarist sits facing his audience, need not rely on any accompanist; if anything goes wrong he can snatch up the instrument with one hand and protect himself with the other. Violinists are hopelessly vulnerable with something in either hand and their expensive and fragile instrument only supported by their chin and shoulder pressure. The need for an accompanist is exceedingly unfortunate if a therapist has no time in which to rehearse. On the other hand if he has, it is the greatest delight. But each instrument has its advantages and disadvantages and the instrument to which a player is drawn is usually the one on which he expresses himself best.

In the chapter on private practice I have given suggestions for instruments for home use. Here I will describe instruments which can be used in hospital in another way. Basically there are three

50

kinds of instrument: blown, percussive and stridulatory. In nature these correspond to the sounds made by calling birds, by rabbits communicating the presence of danger to each other by their warning thumps on the ground and by the whirring sound of the male grasshopper rubbing the file on his left wing-case against the drum on his right wing-case to attract his silent mate. Psychologically one could say that they approximate to Freud's three areas of infantile sexual development: oral, anal and genital. It is interesting to note that these three kinds of instrument have been in use since the very early paleolithic times and are used by most primitive tribes existing today. Significantly enough it is the third category of instrument that the therapist needs least in hospital. String instruments require a keen ear and greater skill and sensitivity in performance. In hospital, as a rule, there is not the time or possibility of practice to make learning a stringed instrument possible, apart from work with guitars or chordal dulcimers. However, patients who already play bowed instruments can always continue and enjoy chamber music.

Here are some notes on other instruments: *Pianos* are often given to the hospital when they should have been given to the garbage dump. The music therapist must fight against letting such geriatric monsters in at all costs and get the existing ones out as fast as he can. They cannot be tuned to concert pitch so no fixed-pitch instrument can play with them. The violinist who has to tune his violin three semitones down is in misery. If he has perfect pitch then his dilemma is even worse. Such instruments are untherapeutic to both music therapists and patients alike. To be expected to use them in therapeutic work is like one of the doctors being handed a nine-inch length of wood instead of a stethoscope. Good pianos must be cherished and in the overheated hospital atmosphere an electric humidifier in their environment would be well worth the outlay. *Small side drums* are useful for beginning to express feelings to the musical containment of the piano. Plastic heads are cheaper than skin but give a harsher sound. *Cymbal on a stand* should be as large as can be afforded. It gives a very satisfying feeling of utmost destruction combined with reassuring physical survival when played with a soft-headed stick. With a wire brush it can give subtle stridulatory effects. *Chromatic xylophone* (and I do not mean a metalaphone or glockenspiel with metal plates) offers melodic possibilities which add intellectual activity to the emotional percussion, and running the beaters up and down the notes gives a delightfully sensuous form of stridulation. *Chinese gong* needs to be at least twenty inches across. It is a very satisfying instrument which gives a tremendously prolonged response to one short blow. It can be taken as the sound embodiment of the fact of the enormous repercussions of a rightly or wrongly directed word or deed. *Chime bars* are useful on the wards for pentatonic improvisations with the therapist. Especially useful for patients who fear the possible ugliness of their sound expression, *Kalimba* is always beautiful and consonant, being tuned in thirds (provided the therapist keeps it tuned with a coin), though the actual playing is rather an aggressive action, difficult for rheumaticky hands. *Glockenspiel* has a delicate and beautiful tone for those who enjoy controlled playing. *Triangles* add just a cold touch to an ensemble. *Bongos or Moroccan pottery drums* are companionable twin drums which are useful for rhythmic conversations, one person to each drum, on the ward or in individual sessions. *Tambourines* express lively excitement when shaken, can take quite a beating and sound mysterious when scratched. *Melodica* is a simple chromatic wind instrument each of whose keys produces one note, set out like a piano keyboard. The larger model, which looks like a tiny piano, is much easier to play. It can be very expressive, is capable of playing chords and is excellent for poignant sadness. *Recorder* is much more complicated, requires better co-ordination. It is a genuine instrument with its own repertoire. Useful for therapeutic music lessons or recorder groups. *Chordal dulcimer* is a very pleasant four chord, sixteen string instrument played with a little hammer or with fingers. Suitable for singers wishing to accompany themselves on something simpler than a guitar. Gentle, soothing sound. *Autoharp* is a more complicated version of the same kind of instrument. There is too much to go wrong for it to be very practical. *Mouth organ* like toothbrushes should not be shared. However they are most useful in that as long as the patient is breathing she cannot fail to make some sound. *Piano accordion* is rather complicated for general use without tuition but a welcome addition if donated to the hospital's instrument collection.

Making instruments

In some hospitals there are facilities for the patients to make musical instruments and there is great satisfaction in playing in a public performance on an instrument which you knew when it was a tin can and an inner tube. Possible instruments with full instructions for making up are contained in *Musical Instruments Made to be*

Played by Ronald Roberts, under whose guidance I made several of my own instruments. Other easily made instruments might include empty painted washing-up-liquid containers filled with split peas to make maraccas; two-inch-diameter bamboo sections with a narrow slit sawn out lengthwise and used to rub against the filed ridges as in the South American guiro; large tin cans with rubber inner tubes secured as drum heads; two two-inch squares of wood with half-inch pieces glued round the edge to make clappers sounding like horses' hoofs in action; and then tubular bells of metal piping cut at different tuned lengths and hung on a wooden frame. Some patients have even made and learnt to play their own violins. The music therapists may be able to combine with the occupational therapists on an instrument-making project.

The music therapist and the instruments
For ward work it is handy to fill a portable shopping trolley with drums, tambourines, maraccas, wrist bells, triangles, chime bars and beaters and anything else that will be wanted and wheel it from ward to ward as needed.

Whenever a new kind of instrument is purchased, the music therapist should endeavour to set apart a little time in which to improvise on it and make it a natural and known vehicle of expression before using it for therapy. Only by trying to reproduce a genuine emotion can he discover its limitations and expressive possibilities. He should also experiment, with colleagues, to find out just how this instrument can combine with others in a group to produce different sound effects expressing diverse moods.

MECHANICAL EQUIPMENT
At least one stationary stereo record player and one portable one will be required by the Music Therapy Department. A portable mains and battery tape recorder with a footage counter is useful for use in the music room, on wards and for meetings. Many patients are very affected when they hear their own music played back to them. While they are playing the music is being produced semi-consciously through the power of their emotion. When it is played back they can evaluate it consciously. A quiet, depressed woman patient who told me repeatedly that she was not an emotional person, was forced to agree that she might be wrong when we listened to her clashing on the cymbal, beating the drum and careering up and down the xylophone. Another patient, a man in his thirties, was so affected by

53

hearing his music that he temporarily experienced physically the unpleasant psychosomatic symptoms which had been the subject of his improvisation and the cause of their removal. It is useful for the therapist to be able to say, "What were you feeling just then?" and find out what a certain change of musical mood or instrument meant to the patient. Tapes of a series of improvisations, together with case notes, form invaluable records of how the music first expresses the later manifested personality and behaviour changes.

For ward work a valuable device is the portable integrated circuit containing a battery, microphone and amplifier. It can let a frail geriatric patient or timid adolescent girl hear her song flooding through the ward as if she were a real prima donna and give her some affirmative feedback as to her identity and ability to please others through her music.

Also to be taken into account are the acoustics of the music room. Some psychotic patients, in particular, can be extremely sensitive to over-resonance; tense patients, too, cannot tolerate harsh or loud sounds. However, too much absorption by carpets, curtains and cushions can make playing an onerous, joyless business in the dead atmosphere.

Lastly I will quote my teacher, the practical as well as idealistic Mme Juliette Alvin who wrote in *Music Therapy*, "The budget of a music department should be well balanced to provide for the essentials, including the first of them, the therapists' remuneration. Too often the money is found for expensive tools and the vital human factor is forgotten, a situation we have found in a number of institutions." Even practising his instrument at home for a minimum of one hour a day, five days a week, a music therapist is putting in over eighty-three three-hour sessions a year, or thirty-two and a half eight-hour days of unpaid work. When, as an analytical music therapist, he adds to this the time taken and money spent on his analysis or analytical psychotherapy, it can be understood that the vital human factor repays the community with interest by being remembered realistically.

Part Two

Practical Experiences and Techniques

6. The big, back ward

This is described as a refractory ward. The adjective is not used here in the dictionary's interpretation of being "unruly, unmanageable, obstinate and perverse" but rather of being "resistant to ordinary treatment and stimulus". Many of the long-stay patients living here became ill before modern chemotherapy was available and their condition at present is considered to be irreversible. This is the end of the line. This is where – in the words of one of my outpatients – "They sit in rows with slides in their hair and thighs like the Post Office Tower waiting only for the next meal". This fate is the secret dread of every patient coming in to a psychiatric hospital. If it were more often voiced patients could be reassured. But it hovers in silence and mounting dread as their treatment is drawn out.

For the music therapist, working in this ward is a sharp challenge to everything that he believes in. The first exposure to these patients – the smells of urine, excrement and foetid breath, the grotesque physical ugliness of some of them, the frozen attitudes of anxiety, aggression and apathy, the pale ivory skin colouring, the misshapen bodies with vast pendulous breasts, unhindered by bras, sagging on to bulging abdomens which in turn rest on huge thighs with their stockings knotted half-way down – it is quite a severe shock. "What is the meaning of life when it is spent twiddling your fingers together and staring anxiously into space?" is the kind of thought that creeps into the music therapist's mind as he unlocks the ward door at the end of the stone-flagged passage. Should he be spending his limited time in here, when he could be helping short-stay patients to come to terms with their troubling emotions and go back to a productive life? These are questions which every music therapist must face.

I feel that just because this is such a stagnant backwater in the life of the hospital, and – in as far as we are all united at a certain level – in the life of the community, it is right and desirable to do everything possible to improve the quality of life of the individuals living on this level and to inspire, encourage and raise the morale and self-esteem of the staff who must care for their daily, and nightly, needs and do so often with admirable devotion, patience and tenderness. In raising the level of consciousness and awareness in this ward – even a fraction – the whole level of being of the hospital is raised. It becomes a healthier place to work in, to train in, to get better in, to live in or even just to visit.

Having struck that fine high note, I will now admit that, at the practical level, working in this ward is not easy. In opening oneself to share joy in movement to live music and musical communication with these patients one too easily carries away some of their burden of apathy and despair. The therapist needs firm connections with his own sources of hope and life. Although the patients could benefit from a bi-weekly music session, this ward is alternated with another long-stay ward and has a bi-monthly session. It is not ideal but it is something.

THE SESSION

Today I am assisting Miss K., the Senior Music Therapist, in this session. The large sitting room contains a grand piano three-quarters of a tone flat, TV, carpeted centre and a double row of arm chairs all round on blue lino, facing the middle except for the south row which faces the TV. "Better get some fresh air in here," says Miss K. and, for once, I agree. It is stifling and oppressively warm. But behind the physical heat is the feeling of psychological stagnation. There are about twenty-five patients sitting in the chairs, all the brighter ones have gone down to work in the Industrial Unit. Miss K. opens windows and I turn the TV chairs round.

Back at the piano, Miss K. says, "I think we'll slowly wake them up," and she stealthily plays an undulating waltz. I sit in a chair behind her beside Nanna, a short, fat woman who seems like a gross caricature of a two-year-old. She has been in this ward for fifty-four years. She looks at me. We smile. She pulls off her left shoe and pulls out a pink and blue ribbon. "Did you give me those?" she asks in her clipped treble voice. "No, Nanna, not those. But I gave you some last Christmas." "Last Christmas," she echoes playing with the ribbons and fraying the ends industriously. The music is filtering through the dead atmosphere. I go down the east line of chairs and stand smiling in front of one patient, my hands outstretched, palms upward. She is curled up in her chair, foetal style, she shakes her head angrily. I accept her rejection with a nod. The next patient is vast, eyes expressionless as a crocodile's in her pale yellow face, but she puts into my hands her own ice-cold leathery palms. There is one finger missing. Gently we swing our hands to the music. She stares up at me without a trace of expression, the hands are heavy but willing. The waltz is becoming more alive. The next patient, Rose, is tiny, the size of a frozen nine-year-old. Her hands are like those of a starving child, all skin and bone, her arms are very tense when she swings and her eyes solemnly look at mine. It is strange how this eye-gazing, one of the first forms of communication of a newborn child, is the last to die out.

Zena, a voluntary helper who is a mature ex-patient, comes in wheeling our basket of instruments. "Would you like to distribute them, Zena?" I ask. "You know these patients better than I do." Miss K. plays rhythmic old songs such as: "Hallo, who's your lady friend?", "Lily of Laguna", and "The Man who broke the Bank at Monte Carlo". There is a very purposeful, united beat coming from here and there around the ward, and at least one patient is singing some of the words. I go round the chairs playing a tambourine, stopping in front of each player who has a percussion instrument to give her the feeling of playing to someone and with someone as these patients scarcely interact sitting, as they do, in long straight lines. Zena helps an athetoid spastic patient to join in by attaching bells to her writhing wrists. The pulsing energy coming from the instruments stirs the atmosphere with life but it is only a resonating sub-group. There is still a hard core of immobile seated patients with their attention directed inwards in some kind of dumb, numb state of existence.

The blonde Spanish Sister comes in with two nurses and Miss K. greets them. "See if you can get them on their feet," she says to me, starting to play a conga rhythm. Starting with the patients who don't mind swinging arms, Zena and I gradually collect ten patients who come and dance in a conga chain. The Sister and nurses join in too with a good deal of laughter. I go to get Nanna. "No dance. Operation," she says. It may have been forty years ago but I let her sit and play with her ribbons. "Oky, Coky?" she asks. "Yes, we'll do the Hoky Coky for you, Nanna," says Miss K. Zena and I arrange the patients in a ring. There is an atmosphere of enjoyment, smiling eyes, a sense of being in on something but a slight feeling of bewilderment, too, on some patients' faces as they fail to keep up with the actions. Next we dance "Here we go round the Mulberry Bush". For a moment I feel a bit idiotic showing the way I "brush my teeth", with only Zena, to the French and African nurses and Spanish Sister and ten patients but then I see that at least one patient is managing to "wash her hands" and the foreign staff are getting the idea and I feel better.

As the patients are taken back to their seats, Edith, a white-haired pear-shaped patient, sits down at the piano, puts her head back with an air of superiority and gives an imitation of a display of keyboard virtuosity. "Lovely, Edith! Do it again," I exclaim. She does it again. "Very nice. Do some more!" This time Edith actually looks at the keyboard and plays individual notes with different fingers up and down the keyboard. It is a perfect example of development through encouragement. Miss K. congratulates her as she comes back to the piano. "Will you sing for us, Jean?" she asks. Jean is very small, so like a child in manner (though adult) that I feel quite shocked to see her smoking. She stands very straight and sings, "If those lips could only speak", in a pleasant voice, well in tune. Some of the listening patients show a flicker of interest. Edith is now sitting and knitting.

Miss K. asks me to play my violin. I have brought the *Spanish Dance* of Granados. The tambourines and drums give me a merciless but rhythmic beat. The Sister applauds enthusiastically. "I know his daughter in Spain," she says. What an astonishing place to meet a friend of Granados' daughter! We have a little talk while Zena and one of the nurses collect the instruments. There are wild screams from one lady. "Go away! It's mine! Go away!" she shouts, protecting the maracca which she has hidden by pushing it into her stocking. She flays round wildly with arms and legs. "Let her keep it," says Miss K. but the coloured nurse succeeds in extracting it and brings it triumphantly back to the basket.

It is time for something quiet. We play an *Andante Cantabile* by Tartini. Rose, the tiny patient with whom I swung hands, gets out of her chair and walks slowly towards me. I play from music so I cannot look at her without losing my place. The little figure comes nearer and nearer and stands quite close to me. I risk a look. Her eyes are intensely searching mine and her arms are folded tightly across her chest. The beautiful serene melody floats out across the ward. We finish. The others applaud. I look at Rose and there is silence. "Well, Rose, what did you think of the music?" I ask gently, feeling that we had shared rather a tender moment. Her words are precise like a little gimlet. "I don't like the violin," she says, drilling me with her intense eyes, "it's too squeaky." (Back to the Royal College of Music and the Virtuoso Class of Geneva Conservatoire to have my fees refunded.) "Marvellous!" said Zena,

'"It's the first time I've heard her say anything but 'Glory Hallelujah' since I've been coming to this ward." Whose rejection was this, that she felt that she could now safely pass on to me? It was so beautifully delivered and – ow – I won't pretend that it didn't hurt.

"Where's Mrs E.?" says Sister looking round. "She had a birthday last week and it would be nice to play for her." "She's in her room having a rest. I will fetch her," says a blonde nurse. Miss K. goes out with her. "Have you got some chime bars in the basket?" I ask Zena. She finds a pentatonic scale of notes and a beater. I go to the piano and play "Onward Christian Soldiers" as Miss K. enters with an understanding look on her face as Mrs E. says, "I've been coming to this church for forty years." She sits in a chair with the chime bars on a little table in front of her. I take up my violin, and Miss K. and I play "Happy Birthday to You". Mrs E., small and pink and white with her shining hair still showing traces of strawberry blonde, seems to exist in another dimension. She is there and yet somehow she seems to be far away as well. She beams at the birthday music. "I am one hundred and three years old," she says. "Will you play us a tune for your birthday?" I ask. "I'll play with you." I quickly tune my violin the three-quarters of a tone up to the pitch of the chime bars. She takes the beater and starts beating solemnly, note after note, as if it were a hymn. I improvise in the pentatonic scale. (At this point the patients from the Industrial Unit come in for their tea and gather round. One pretty young deaf mute goes over to Miss K., her face shining with happiness, she pulls up her little skirt and points triumphantly to her stocking suspenders. Yes, she's the only one in the ward who has them. Will she have a bra, too, I wonder, or lose her figure in thirty years' time like the others?) Gradually old Mrs E.'s playing becomes more and more adventurous, she sways about as she beats until together we create quite a little Dionysian rhapsody. She ends up by throwing the beater on the floor and her arms around Miss K. whom she kisses noisily on the cheek. Everyone claps except the hard core of unmovable patients. But the atmosphere has changed, the ward has become part of life and the community. We are twenty minutes late for our tea and there is another tough ward ahead but it has been worth it.

THOUGHTS ABOUT WORKING IN A REFRACTORY WARD

The chief enemy here, for the therapist, is meaninglessness. It is essential for him not to be seduced away from that which makes his work meaningful to himself by any empty theory or idea however useful this may be to another person in another situation. His main aim should be to retain hope, sensitive empathy and enthusiasm. If he can do this, the quality of his therapeutic work will guarantee results. If he only goes out for results, in the form of response and co-operation, from the patients, he will lose the dignity of his own communication of meaning to them and most likely find himself a victim of the despair, apathy and uselessness with which they will infect him.

It is almost impossible to treat this kind of ward as one whole group. Better results are obtained from forming small sub-groups whose members can interact with the therapist and each other in dancing or playing on percussion instruments. Here people do not get restless if the therapist goes round to each one in turn with chime bars and a melodic instrument and creates as many little individual musical communications as possible. In this way just one therapist can start the ward work off, finding out who will communicate verbally, musically or by movement. Then a colleague can join him when he is ready to create group situations.

Every ward has its talents: someone will sing, someone recite, someone play an instrument or possibly one of the nurses will contribute a musical item. It is up to the therapist to use all the available material as creatively and receptively as he can.

The dancing, I believe, should be done only if the therapist is willing and happy to join in. His active and joyous participation makes it a meaningful activity to the patients. If he were to stand aside and urge them to dance without himself taking part, it would be faintly insulting and pointless – if not impossible. When the therapist and ward staff are dancing too, enough energy and enthusiasm is engendered to bear the apathy of the patients up and over the point of inertia. The eye and hand contact of the therapist are vitally important aspects of the communication of the dance. While the music, with its shared rhythm, unites them all inwardly at the level of the collective unconscious, the warm, live hand touch and eye contact lures these patients out into a greater acceptance of a shared outer reality.

"Don't you find it depressing?" is a question often asked about work in just this kind of ward. If the therapist looks around at the scene as an inanimate observer then it is, indeed, desperately depressing. But if he sees himself as a channel of life and love and energy bringing the care of the community into this turbid environment then he is witnessing the most hopeful thing that could happen. His responsibility is great, his task is to inject meaning into meaninglessness. He must not, at all costs, lose his ability to vibrate truly in accordance with the sources of his deepest inner harmony, whatever they may be.

7. The locked female ward

This is a ward which needs its weekly music therapy session very badly. Here communication uses the interlinking element of emotional expression through sound to share feelings which are otherwise experienced intrapersonally through hallucinations or autistic fantasies. Speaking to patients in other parts of the hospital one realises that this ward is the bogy-man – the police ward – for the whole of the female side. "Any more of that and you'll go up to Cherry Tree ward," is the threat. And that does not make it any easier for those who work there. For a certain percentage of stagnated long-stay patients, it makes little difference. Though it may be the ultimate dungeon experience to fellow patients undergoing a "holding" period (usually experienced as punitive), to these residents it is home. Other people come in in a state of wild excitement or stunned withdrawal, stay for a while changing character dramatically and then leave just as they have become integrated into the ward routine; but no flood tide of life washes these long-stay patients back into the outside world. As emissaries of the larger world we enter this ward to seduce them into accepting a little part of a reality which admits the creative possibilities of fantasy when it is used in the service of sharing human feelings through art.

THE SESSION
Today my colleague Miss V., a pianist and clarinettist, is with me. Or, strictly speaking, I am with her. We usually decide which of us will take the session to avoid confusion in making decisions. Today it is her turn. The ward is vast and open plan. There are doors leading off it to north, south, east and west. The small patch of carpet in the sitting area does not seem to do anything to mute the echoing resonance of footsteps going in all directions. In some of the armchairs pushed back against the wall patients are curled up like cats in foetal position, their feet tucked up under their bodies and their eyes tight shut. It always amazes me that the perennial need for this phase of withdrawn expression is not faced realistically by hospital

authorities. Why not have some comfortable and evocative foetal chairs designed and made for patients in this phase? The one thing that patients are not permitted to do in hospital, it seems, is to have their illness, which, after all, *is* their present reality however bizarre, threatening, unacceptable or inconvenient it may be to those who have to have their own, quite different working life reality alongside it. But I am digressing.

Miss V. moves the piano to an angle where she can see the patients and I help re-arrange the chairs from neat rows to a large circle. From the west door there is thumping and muffled shouts. "Who's that?" Miss V. asks Zoe, a small, long-stay victim of manic-depression in a quiet phase. "It's Betty, she's in the pads again," says Zoe philosophically. She is herself very familiar with the padded cell. Miss V. goes over to have a word with the trim, well groomed Indian Ward Sister and a moment later Betty emerges holding on to a motherly West Indian nurse. Betty is in her sixties, small, toothless, plump, her eyes full of suffering and anger and her grey dishevelled hair in a long pigtail hanging down her towelling dressing-gown.

"Hello Betty! Glad you could come to music therapy. Would you sing us a song?" Miss V. says. Betty blinks and mutters something. Miss V. goes and takes her arm and brings her over to the piano. "Sing the one about the Spaniard," pleads another long-stay patient. Betty turns with a little smile. Her head rises proudly as she sings an indignant song with spirited threats of violence, her eyes flashing fire but her body sagging and uninvolved with the expression. Miss V. adds a few gentle chords to support but not cover her singing. We all clap enthusiastically. Betty smiles and sits down peacefully. This way her aggression is accepted.

Barbara is a short-stay manic-depressive patient in her forties from another ward. I see that she is sitting looking almost greenish-white with some kind of distress, and I go up and say that I am sorry to find her here and we chat. Meanwhile Miss V. has distributed the drums, tambourines and maracas to those who will accept them and improvises some music in a Spanish idiom. I stand in the centre with a sawn-off chair leg and the wooden rim of an old tambourine (we are always short of instruments) and I exchange rhythmic communication and establish eye contact with those who are ready to receive it. Over at the north side of the ward, Audrey, a woman in her forties, is standing talking to herself and acting out some scene with hallucinatory characters and then running up and down wringing her hands. A little blonde nurse tries to get her to sit down but fails. Every now and then a paranoid schizophrenic long-stay patient sitting by the wall swears darkly at her when she comes too close. A young Indian lady in a beautiful lilac sari holds her long black pigtail; she sits in the circle but is quietly murmuring something in her own language throughout the session.

Next I play the *Allegro in G* by Fiocco on my violin accompanied by Miss V. This ward has one of the two hospital pianos which are at concert pitch. It is a joy not to have the violin strings rattling round the fingerboard and to have the customary bow/string tension relationship. The percussion accompaniment is lively and rhythmical, following the piano.

"Was that Johann Sebastian Bach?" asks Nelly, another moodswing victim of vast proportions. She has latched on to this name and wants all music to be that. "No, Nelly, but it was from the same period, the beginning of the eighteenth century." Nelly gives a triumphant nod to her neighbour. "Can I come up and play you a bit of Johann Sebastian Bach?" she asks. Miss V. says, "Yes, please do." Nelly seats herself firmly at the piano. She concentrates, raises her arms and plays an imaginative and expressive atonal improvisation. "Oh, shut up, Nelly, you know you can't play the piano," snaps Ruth, another long-stay patient. We clap. "Thank you, Nelly, I liked your music," says Miss V. Nelly gives Ruth another triumphant look. I collect up the percussion instruments and then we begin the beautiful Fiocco *Arioso*. Over in the east side of the ward, out of the corner of my eye I see a man pushing a body on a stretcher. Goose pimples. It moves. Good, it is alive, I think. Barbara is now weeping copiously and looking a much better colour. The slow pieces very often release sorrow with good results. "What did you think of that music?" asks Miss V. "Peaceful." "Sad." "It is the first time in ever so long that I have been able to cry and it was marvellous," said Barbara. "Can I play one of your compositions, Barbara?" asks Miss V. who has brought the music which she took down in dictation from Barbara's playing in an individual session. "Can you play the one called 'Melancholy'?" asks Barbara. Miss V. plays it with a great deal of feeling and everyone claps enthusiastically. Barbara suddenly comes to life. "I believe I could play it now myself," she says, having mopped herself up. She comes to the piano and plays the piece with much more fury and hesitation, the difference is most striking. We clap. Barbara looks pleased and hopeful again.

A long-stay schizophrenic lady with two large round patches of blue make-up on her cheeks comes up and whispers to Miss V. "Yes, certainly, Enid," answers Miss V. Enid tries to play something on the piano, it is clearly something she once knew but it is chaotic and distorted now. She breaks off looking unhappy and bewildered. "Could you sing it to us?" asks Miss V. in her gentle voice. Enid faces the circle and sings, "I love chocolate . . ." over and over again. We clap and she goes smiling to her seat.

A man with a machine-powered trolley goes noisily through the ward from south to east. A young schizophrenic girl stands by the window anxiously spying for dreaded parachutes. Audrey runs up and down near her and twitters. We sing several songs together but voices are weak. "Who would like to sing us a solo?" asks Miss V. A new patient, Iris, in a dressing-gown volunteers. She chooses a song with a chorus which everyone joins in. "Can I sing 'Loch Lomond'?" asks Irene, an obese young long-stay patient whose sluggish exterior hides homicidal tendencies. As she stands singing her head lifts, her slouch vanishes and she achieves a touching, almost sculptural dignity. The man with the machine-powered trolley comes through again, this time from east to south. Why doesn't the fellow hurry up and get out? Then I look and see that he has stopped and is listening to the music. Suddenly I feel that this is not a locked ward full of banished souls but the very centre of the world. It is the eternal man stopping work for a moment to hear the eternal woman sing. I cherish this moment.

The applause breaks the spell. Nelly spies the man with the trolley and runs over to kiss him but he has the motor started and is out of the door in a flash. "Can you play us a waltz?" asks Nelly turning back philosophically. Miss V. plays a swinging waltz. I get up and dance with Nelly and she puffs and grunts her way enthusiastically round the ward giving me much needed instructions as to where to put my feet. Miss V. changes to a jazzy tune. Two other patients join us to make a circle. And now the music has penetrated where nothing else did. Down at the east end of the ward Audrey is rocking and rolling in perfect time to the music. She is united with the group through the rhythm, throwing her whole self into the dance. Lily, a slender subnormal girl, joins her, dancing with tremendous verve on legs like matchsticks and smiling and looking from side to side with her great big dark eyes.

Four more patients join our circle. I am as vague as they are about the correct movements but we smile, cold leathery hands are held warmly and somehow the dance brings pleasure. Several more patients come up and join in. Hands reach out to welcome them. I see the consultant psychiatrist standing quietly by the south door. At last we stop. "It's nice to see you getting them all active," says the consultant. It was not me but the music. Miss V. is talking to Barbara, Enid and Nelly in turn. I pack up my violin. "Goodbye, thank you for coming." "Goodbye, where is Miss K. this week?" "Beechside ward." "Give her my love." "I will." "My brother used to play the violin. He died in the war. He was the best brother you ever could imagine. It was never the same after he left us. My mother can't bear to hear the violin. But I like it. . . ." It is often difficult to make the break from Cherry Tree ward.

THOUGHTS ABOUT SESSIONS IN THIS KIND OF WARD

In this ward the need is more for individual achievement through expression and the feeling of self-esteem given by applause, than for a group experience. Here everything is done in a group: eating, sleeping, sitting, going to the canteen, ward meetings and so on and on. The therapist encourages patients to come forward and contribute by the way in which he receives all the others bold enough to do so. They see that it is safe to communicate through music or dance and they venture into participation. Words follow.

The character of the ward will change from week to week. At one time there may be two or three manic patients whose excitement must be contained within the structure of the session. Dancing is a useful outlet here. It is much better to put the energy into good expression rather than to attempt to thwart it as it easily turns to violence. If there is more than one patient in the manic stage it can sometimes be unwise to use percussion instruments as, if they get thrown into the air, the assistant music therapist could conceivably catch one at a time but hardly more. And a tambourine is a nasty thing to land on your head when you are busy playing the piano.

The ward may be very apathetic and depressed, in which case it is wise to join the patients in this mood and gradually introduce music which expresses the violence and energy which is locked away beneath the depression. It is beneficial, too, for these patients to have some exercise, either dancing or moving freely to music, as it has been shown that this often helps to lift the depression a little.

Patients with a talent or liking for music can be invited to join one of the other music groups in the hospital with the Sister's assent, and enjoy a wider life experience through meeting people from other wards and joining in the monthly concerts.

To these very disturbed patients emotion has been so damaging that they need all the usefully channelled rewarding emotional experiences that they can get. Through music they can identify with feelings that they have cut off through their illness, as Barbara regained her capacity for tears.

The music therapists must be the bridge between the real world, cut off by the locked doors, and the ward life; and also between the invisible dissociated parts of the patient's psyche and the visible self that presents itself to others. We must live in two worlds and somehow realise their oneness, and it is music that enables us to do this.

8. The locked male ward

A weekly music therapy is desirable in wards of this kind. This is a locked ward for disturbed male patients, many of them with a record of violence. Fortnightly visits would be too widely spaced to have much cumulative effect. Twice-weekly visits would possibly permit a more constructive, musically creative approach but if the hospital's therapist/patient ratio is low, weekly visits are adequate. For best results two music therapists should work together. This ward has 39 patients. All these patients are never together having music therapy, a few are doing chores, ill in bed, locked up in side rooms or sitting and writing letters. But it is difficult for a therapist to sit with his back in close proximity to a group of very unpredictable individuals and give his fullest attention to them through the music. It can be done and I, and many others, have done it but it is a strain, and music, patients, therapy and the therapist all suffer unnecessarily in the process.

This is a rough impression of a typical session. Mr O., the pianist music therapist, is with me, pushing a basket of drums, tambourines and other small percussion instruments along in front of him. As we enter the ward territory there are greetings from some of the patients and we cheerfully return them. We look in at the Charge Nurse's office and he says he will be coming in when he has finished his paper work. It is not that we need him for disciplinary purposes but it makes a good atmosphere for the ward staff to share the music. A young male nurse is in the sitting area. Chairs are already grouped round the piano in several semicircular rows, and as we move the piano so that Mr O. can see the audience (at least out of the corner of his eye) the television is switched off and the men begin to occupy the seats.

Not waiting for perfect peace and order, Mr O. sits down at the piano and rather quietly begins to play Schubert's *Impromptu in A flat*. It is expedient to start with some really good music in order to change the atmosphere of the ward and set the key for the session. This is like a call going out to those who can respond to it. These people settle down quicker, sit very still and absorb the music hungrily. I mark them, they are useful group resonators. Gradually most of the others follow them. The nurse tells some very withdrawn patients in the corners to move. And they do.

The piano is appalling. It is a whole tone flat and painfully out of tune but the music overcomes even this and soars up into an emotional sunlight pouring out its sweetness and beauty. A man in the front row sits with his head hanging desolately down and his elbows on his thighs. He has sat thus throughout every session so far. Does he hear the Schubert? Does it penetrate his prison of depression? Does he, himself, feel as utterly useless as he makes us feel? However much we would like to explore this it is not possible in this larger group session.

The applause brings me back to my role function. Now we will release some of the violent inner music of this group. Mr O. starts to play a rousing march and I take drums, tambourines, maracas and cymbals out of the shopping trolley and walk along the line of men. I give an instrument to anyone who asks or reaches for one, to those whose limbs moved in time to the music, to anyone in a tense, arms-folded, legs-crossed position and then I gently use this offering of instruments as an excuse to receive the rejection of the withdrawn patients who do not want to join in. This may be their only communication during the session but the therapist's willing acceptance of it may make it easier for them, in turn, to accept what they experience as someone else's rejection of themselves. As usual there are not enough instruments to go round. But those that are in use pound out the rhythm with a power that is quite frightening. The rhythm takes over and seems to have a group expression of desperate earnestness. It is like the sound of a grim, relentless army. I tune my violin down to F, C, G, and D, so that I can read the top line at the piano's pitch. The gaiety and liveliness in the faces of the percussion players is in sharp contrast to their rugged music. All the sour, deadness of the atmosphere is lifting.

I feel that this powerful, mindless emotional group expression wants an admixture of discriminating thought. "Who wants to be a conductor?" I ask. Two men come up. One has wide, excited eyes and he cannot stop talking. He grabs the little baton and starts to tell an obscene story about a bus conductor. Bert suffers from manic-depression and is in a sad life situation. When his story is finished I say, "Would you rather Bob conducted first so that you know what to do?" He agrees and sits down amicably. "Bob is going to tell us all when to play really loudly. Show us what you are going to do for loud," I say. He beats with giant movements. He demonstrates pianissimo, too. There is a minute's silence while Bob waits for Mr O. to begin and Mr O. waits for him. Then Bob realises that he really is the conductor, gives us the beat and off we go. His wardmates watch him keenly, playing loud and soft, all but one old man in a peaked-cap who keeps up a healthy forte beat on his drum throughout and continues several bars after everyone else has finished. I must remember to ask the Charge Nurse if he is deaf or just showing signs of senile perseverance. The mindless group giant has gone, it is now a group of individuals.

It is time to play. "We are going to create our own music, a kind of sound picture. Who has an idea for a story?" A big man, previously silent but shaking with laughter, suddenly answers: "A vampire." At this moment a group of four medical staff in white coats come in, give us a look which I experience as withering, and walk slowly through the ward on their way to the far dormitory. (Why couldn't he have chosen something wholesome and respectable like last week's Autumn Bonfires? Nothing to do but plod resolutely on.) There is some anxiety about the presence of the doctors. I struggle for the group's attention. "What does the vampire do?" "He lives in a castle." "He flies in to windows of bedrooms and sucks the blood of beautiful young girls." ". . . beautiful young girls. I see. What else?" The doctors are now forgotten. "He has a troop of wolves." "He goes to the churchyard and sleeps in a grave." "When the bell rings he goes home to the castle." I collect the elements and intone the story phrase by phrase interspersed by vampire, wolf, shrieking girl, bell and castle music created by various patients to the accompaniment of Mr O.'s atonal improvisation and the occasional banshee wail on my violin. The men's percussion sounds are sensitive and mysterious, quite different from their marching fervour. There is a feeling of tension and intensity. It is a structured spontaneity which absorbs everyone's attention except the patient looking at the floor. The man who suggested the title laughs silently. I must find out if this is one of the more bizarre forms of schizophrenia or some kind of manic defence. No time to think about that now. I resin my bow.

Something has been created, there is space for other impressions to enter. Curiously enough I have Sibelius' *Valse Triste* for violin and piano with me which rather suits the mood of the moment. I announce it, and Mr O. and I play with all the despair and abandonment of Bert's illness. It is quiet before they clap. A wonderful deep hush. "What did you feel about that piece?" I ask. "Sad." "Happy." "My uncle used to play the violin, only as an amateur. He never played that though." There are suggestions as to what the story might be. Next we play Albert Roussel's beautiful and gently sensuous *Aria* over a thirsty silence. I feel the music going in right where it is needed. When I play to these men I feel I must practise harder, go right in to the depths of my own feelings to find there the essence that they need. I am grateful for the quality of their listening, not defensive, critical listening but a real appetite for the experience behind the music. One must not fail them by offering them empty cleverness, pleasant sounds and slick virtuosity. They clap heartily and I respond sincerely to this gesture with Mr O. They do not have a lot to give in this place, what there is must be cherished.

The violin solos pave the way for individual expression. "Who else would like to play or sing something?" I ask, stretching my arms out. A turbanned gentleman with a long, thin face and snow-white moustache and beard comes up and sits at the piano with all the dignity of a Rubinstein. Bert rushes up to join him but Mr O. persuades him to sit down. We have no mutual language so we have no idea of what to expect. With solemnity and florid grandeur he proceeds to improvise atonally, sweeping up and down the piano and often finishing with a few knocks on the wood above and below the keyboard. I am certain that he has never touched a piano in his life before and is just copying Mr O. Professor Alfred Nieman, our teacher, would have been delighted with his sparkling dissonances. It is clearly a very meaningful and personally expressive happening. The patients sit rapt with attention. Only the nurse laughs.

While we were playing marches I had noticed one man whose beat was sophisticated and alive. I pick him out and ask if he could sing us something. Some of the other men shout "Play us a tune, Sandy." "I'm shy," he says and turns his back. But finally we all persuade him to play on his mouth-organ some songs that everyone English knows. He plays well, employing a tongued accompaniment style. Bert gets up and stands beside him, his arm round Sandy's shoulder, singing all the songs at the top of his voice. When Sandy finishes Bert launches into a dubious solo, finishes that, then pulls an older man to his feet. The man, Louis, says thunderously, "You leave me alone." There is a tense moment. I believe they will resolve it. But Mr O. quickly gives Bert a tambourine to make an accompaniment to Louis' rendering of "Land of My Fathers". The danger is passed.

73

How I love my colleagues when they do just the right thing at the right time! It is not good to do this work alone. As the Welsh melody rises and the intensity of expression increases Louis' pitch becomes sharper and sharper. I wince inwardly as he strikes a quarter tone above the piano. There is enthusiastic applause.

A man at the other end of the row has made a puddle on the floor. Before the nurse says anything Bert is there mopping it up and reassuring him. I have many times noticed that there seems to be a spirit of gentle helpfulness to those in trouble on the male wards whereas there is cattiness, exasperation and continual bickering on the female wards. It is as if men without women produce in themselves the most loving female qualities and that women without men produce the most odious masculine attributes.

"Can we have the songbooks, Nurse?" He comes back with songbooks, Charge Nurse and a coloured patient in a dressing gown, too. The atmosphere is now pleasant and relaxed. Mr O. and I feel happy when the medical team troop through once more. Anyone who can read has a songbook and I wait quietly for a number to be called. Because of the drugs making patients' throats so dry, and because of the difference in the cultures represented in the ward, singing is not nearly as good an activity for expression and tension release as percussion music. Even if everyone sings, which they don't, the sound is disappointingly small. However, we often find that withdrawn elderly patients are soundlessly mouthing the words to the old hymns. The ward staff usually enjoy the singing, too.

Bob offers to sing a solo hymn. Bert suddenly sits down and looks desolate. Several people join in. Next I ask a coloured man from the East if he could sing something from his country. "I cannot sing your language," he replies. "Just sing in your own language." He comes out and stands in front of the group with his eyes shut and his head raised and bent slightly back and he chants with an intense, yearning sound with strange musical embroidery. Everyone listens attentively. He is sharing a deep, inner experience which sounds as if it comes from thousands of miles and thousands of years away. When he stops and is applauded I ask, "What is it about?" "It is about my God," he says simply and then, emboldened by his success, asks, "And tell me what is the psychology behind this music therapy?" I answer him with snippets of information about tension release, creativity, communication and socialisation while Mr O. is organising a division of labour in a performance of "Old Macdonald Had a Farm". The staff join in, Bert is in his element

74

again as conductor and there is a lively party atmosphere except for the man who sits looking at the floor. Another coloured man is invited to sing but says with dignity, "In my country either we sing or we are audience." An excitable manic compatriot takes a little table in lieu of a drum and proceeds to give a vigorous display of drumming and chanting "like there was at my brother's wedding". Mr O. improvises a convincing eastern piano accompaniment. The drummer's dressing-gown cords are dancing like golden snakes.

Someone chooses a sea shanty which brings us back to group activity and then, the hour being up, Mr O. and I swing into the national anthem and everyone rises to their feet, some prompted by others. The session is over.

In a large, violent ward of mixed culture as this is, the therapist has to avoid the creation of non-participating sub-groups which may turn into warring elements within the whole. By tapping off the main feelings of aggression through the medium of the trans-racial expression of rhythm, the field is left clear for the group to accept more individual forms of expression. As far as possible the therapists respond to all patients' requests to perform. If special music is needed, if possible they buy it. The atmosphere is generally permissive within clearly defined dykes. For example, I will not permit anyone to play my violin. I explain that the terms of the insurance forbid it. Almost all suggestions are accepted but no patient is allowed to take over the session in such a way that others do not have a chance to share their music. Manic patients, however, are allowed a bit more chance to use their energies in this harmless way even if they are getting rather more than their share of attention while they are high. It is a useful safety valve. Patients are persuaded, but not coerced, into taking part. The expressed wish not to play or sing is respected. Sometimes there is some sexual exhibitionism in this type of ward but if the patient himself is accepted and spoken to and his activities ignored the trouble tends to dwindle and cease. If it does persist – and I once had a most difficult time trying to transpose 'Abide With Me' down a minor third while being distracted by such activities in the front row – then one of the ward staff can be asked to sit by the patient in the back row.

In large wards with shifting populations it is hard enough to get hold of names (first names are generally used in hospitals of this kind as they're more anonymous) let alone the diagnoses. Therefore I have not given all the patients' psychiatric labels unless they are obvious; patients are just treated as their behaviour of the moment warrants. The therapist will soon spot the paranoid schizophrenics and learn to approach them with due care. When a special study of one or two patients is made, the therapist can ask their names and have a word with the Charge Nurse about them after the session. But in a large group session this kind of knowledge is not really necessary. What is important is that we have entered into a genuine group experience which takes account of both the emotional and spiritual needs of people in a way that is often overlooked in an institution of this kind. Too often emotion is thought of as something which only produces ugly and inconvenient scenes and acts; its positive, creative aspects, which are so healing, are just as real. To listen passively to someone singing or playing on the television is a very different thing from helping to create a musical happening with live musicians. A live audience is not merely passive, it is a creative force in the performance of a musician, as anyone who has broadcast from an empty studio will have realised with dismay.

This pattern of changing the atmosphere, releasing the aggression, introducing discrimination and control, setting free creative, spontaneous music-making followed by serious music, individual solos and group songs, is a pattern which has proved successful with this type of ward. This does not mean that it will be right for all wards or all therapists nor that other patterns should not be tried and adopted where they prove effective. The therapists must experiment with and respond to the character and abilities of the group they are working with at the moment.

9. Psychodynamic movement and relaxation session

THE ETIOLOGY

During the early days of my own analytical psychotherapy, before the start of Intertherap, I found it extremely useful to put on suitable records and dance out my feelings concerning fantasies and ideas that we were discussing during the sessions. I found that repressed emotions, hinted at by the psychotherapist, would first appear as body movements and tensions, and with this expression would come a whole host of memories and associations and only then the mental acceptance and full impact of the emotion would come to me. Having experienced these emotions to the limit myself, I found that I could face them without tension in my patients. I became a tunable drum, as it were, able to resonate or not to the patients' vibrations at will. Therefore when Miss K., the senior music therapist, faced me with the need for some kind of movement to music which would give patients an opportunity for more expressive outlets than are offered by any routine physical training, plus the necessity of taking in the current relaxation session (the time for which I was taking), psychodynamic movement and relaxation was conceived. It was to be a new musical technique for encounter, not only between the patient and music therapist but also between the patient and her own body sensations, feelings and thoughts. It was not an easy gestation. Of the three patients allotted to me at the initial session, one was feeling so unwell following her electro-convulsive therapy that she could not come, the second was in such a state of anxiety that she was almost rigid and quite impervious to outside stimuli, and the third was so thin and so cold in the vast airy gym that any kind of relaxation was out of the question. When I reported the dismal doings to Miss K. she promptly said, "Good, we'll put it on twice a week and move it to the music therapy room." Such faith! I rang down to Chichester to an interested psychiatrist engaged in research. "Try rhythm!" he said. We tried. Yes, this was the group-binding, individually-releasing introductory factor that was needed.

Other patients came and they made good use of what we had to offer. There was a giving and taking on all sides. It was born.

The aim of the session is relaxation through awareness and communication. The first kind of communication is the most primitive and natural form: expressive movement. If patients say that they do not know how to do this, the therapist lets them talk a little and then points out the way that they are crossing their legs, pointing their feet, waving their hands around and holding their bodies. They look at the rest of the group standing with arms folded, hands on hips or in between their thighs; they become aware of this form of communication. It is always using them. They can use it.

The leading music therapist uses the group method of psychotherapy within the group. He does not attempt to analyse the group as such as he is expecting each individual to be aware of herself and to be able to share this special awareness. It is an encouragement towards inner-directedness – that is being directed from one's centre – rather than an attempt to be other-directed and try to conform to others. Having first released some of their tension through expressing feelings in movement and words, patients find it easier to relax their bodies.

THE STRUCTURE
The therapist introduces patients (who may come from different wards) by any name they choose to offer. He explains to newcomers the aim of the session. (Personally I do not think that it makes for wholeness to take a person into hospital, treat them as a subnormal parcel, explaining nothing to them, and then wonder why they become anxious, childishly dependent and lacking in enlightened self-interest.) Two music therapists are employed for this hour, one to lead the inquiry and to join in the movement and the other to improvise for the second movement and the relaxation. The first movement is a warm-up in which everyone takes part. Usually lively rhythmic recorded music, such as Latin-American, is used. The leading therapist should avoid giving anything like a display of neat footwork, which would be dutifully copied, but should genuinely draw into himself and get in touch with those body areas which need to be allowed to move. It is wise to get beginners on their feet before the music starts, as otherwise they may not have the courage actually to get up and move. If a patient remains seated, the therapist

can go to her and put out his hands, palms up, and the patient will probably allow herself to be drawn into the dance where she can be released. Patients with sprained ankles, heart conditions, shaky pregnancies and so on, can sit and dance with their arms, hands, feet and head. It is very inhibiting to the group to have non-participants; the only ones we have allowed have been observing psychiatrists who would themselves have had much more inner understanding of the meaning of the session if they had joined in.

When the music is over, the group (which should not exceed seven) sit down and the leading therapist questions them in turn. The structure behind the question is: "What did your body feel like during the movement?" and "What sort of thoughts or ideas did you have that you want to share?" and "What sort of mood were you in?" The purpose of these questions is to stimulate the patient's awareness of these areas of function and to enable her to communicate this to others. It is surprising how many patients cannot, at first, tell you anything about how their bodies feel. Others, again, have given all complaints to their bodies and are unable to report on emotional feelings. A third category are full of enjoyment or misery and body sensations but quite blank concerning thoughts and ideas. As the weeks go by this begins to change most interestingly. The therapist's question becomes the permission to have body sensations, emotions or thoughts, a permission which was perhaps experienced as withheld at some vital early date. The creative frustration of being asked to communicate within this narrow framework brings pressing matters to the surface very forcefully and the therapist can help the group to investigate anything that seems useful.

For the next movement the music is improvised atonally (to avoid any musical associations) in response to the patients' associations to a given stimulus. Usually the therapist lets the patient who is least able to express herself in movement or talking choose the stimulus, so that she makes some investment in the session. Otherwise he asks a new patient, or one whose problem he believes could be helped by a certain area of investigation, or one that he is frankly curious about.

There is something very special about choosing. Somehow it helps to centralise people. While choosing, they get a special look, being at once balanced and strong enough both to reject and select. However emotionally disturbed they are, there is a strong feeling of "This is me doing this choosing. I know what I want, no one's

79

going to pull a fast one on me." The act of choosing puts them in touch with a reliable identity. The fact that the group then abides by this choice and music is improvised for it is very reassuring.

The stimuli which are in present use are a book of coloured felts, a bag of Feelies (tactile stimuli of fur, sandpaper, toy animals, a cotton reel, eraser, metal discs and so on), two long strips of lace for throwing into unguided shapes on which to project images, a collection of sets of word cards (such as seven states of air, fire, water and earth, emotional opposites, unfinished sentences, highway signs, human relationships, different parts of plants and trees and so on), poetry quotations and cabbalistic symbols.

When each patient has given some associations to the stimulus, the playing therapist improvises the music either by conscious association with the ideas expressed by the group or by group counter-transference of those unexpressed feelings causing tension. This music is arhythmic and atonal; it represents the very inchoate inner world and to move to it is to create some kind of meaning and order in that world and allow some of its force to enter an outer form which can be shared. A few patients find this threatening at first. They are used to regarding music as a rhythmic holding structure and now they are asked to give their own structure to the music. But when they get used to it, they find in it a great freedom and the unconscious images experienced through it can be a valuable enrichment of understanding and energy.

For the leading therapist conducting the enquiry there are two problems: patients who will not talk and patients who will not stop talking. He must learn to judge when to sacrifice the group for the individual and when to sacrifice the individual for the group. It is a matter which needs sensitive handling.

After this movement, in which the leading therapist takes part with his own body expression (keeping enough observer faculty going to note how it is with the group), they again sit down and answer the therapist's inquiry. The atmosphere here should be that of a warm, "enabling" group; the music and expression (or non-expression) in movement will do all that is necessary to release hidden feelings. This is not the sort of externally toughening up group where the therapist and group strip one another bare and reveal each other's open wounds with an all-round increase in insensitivity. As the music lays bare the inner sensitivity, the therapist and group form a supportive matrix in which the individual is helped to face these inner feelings alone.

Psychodynamic movement and relaxation session

After this, patients lie on rugs on the floor and the leading therapist goes through a programmed relaxation starting with the potentially aggressive areas of hands and mouth and then going from feet to head, letting the patients silently give the inner instructions to "Let go", to each body area in turn. A simple visualisation is suggested to hold while the music is played. If the therapist does not possess special knowledge and experience with symbols, then any natural images suggesting development and growth are suitable. For example: crocuses flowering on snowy ground, sun rise, star rise, the spring of water flowing to the sea, a bird on its nest, a chick hatching, a candle flame, swallows flying, fields being ploughed and that kind of thing. The playing therapist lets the title influence his music. The leading therapist will watch the respiration of the patients, whether it is deep or shallow, slow or fast, and how much they seem able to relax. Patients with shallow chest breathing may need extra instruction.

THE MUSIC

Improvisation for psychodynamic movement must be conceived at a deep and instinctual level. Here the therapist will contact the organismic waves of dynamic sound patterning which will resonate these same levels in the dancers. His judgement must be sensitive. Five patients have all given associations of sweetness and light to the colour ice blue. How far are they ready to face their frozen fear as the other aspect of it? Only he decides.

When catharsis occurs, which it does quite often with torrential tears or outbursts of anger, he must know when to turn the music into building, holding major triads while the leading therapist deals with the human understanding and verbally accepting part of the situation. At these moments the whole group forms the holding matrix and the usual pattern stops until the patient has fully expressed her feelings and received what assurance the group is able to offer. I never arrange to do this, it just happens and it reminds me of the report of a primitive tribe in South America where the group stand round a woman in labour, protectively, until her child is born. She is alone at her work, as she must be, but held in safety just as I feel that these patients are. This supportive feeling continues outside the session, I have been told. No group member seems to resent the loss of the customary pattern for these group therapeutic occasions. They sense the value of them. The cathartic feeling can resonate in different members of the group so that the therapist can have a similar, though usually lesser, explosion in the following session. So far, every spontaneous cathartic incident seems to have been a genuine nadir of the patient's emotional experience; in spite of warm, permissive handling no patient has become trapped in the pattern or felt the need to repeat it. On the contrary all have gone ahead with greater courage and independence.

Music for relaxation must be very sensitive. Only by feedback from relaxing colleagues or recording his own music and trying to relax to it himself, can the trainee perfect his technique. This music should suggest movement and yet not the kind of movement that makes limbs twitch. It should suggest stillness, yet not the stillness of frozen emotion and stagnation. Most important is for the therapist to put his mind and feelings into a condition of limpid contentment and play from there. He must fill an inner reservoir with this feeling, stealing it drop by drop from life. It helps, too, to follow the relaxation instructions of the leading therapist.

THE PATIENTS

Only patients of a certain intelligence will be able to make use of this therapy. Very paranoid, senile or obsessionally neurotic patients are not usually suitable, nor patients who are too crippled, immobile or fragile to use the movement expression. Otherwise almost any patient with any label has made good use of these sessions. Some experience acute embarrassment during the movement but if the therapist can encourage them to speak about this and compare it with the experience of the other members, it seldom lasts more than six sessions – or three weeks.

THE GROUP

Although this group is specifically for training in awareness, communication and relaxation, and could be called an activity group, yet it may be helpful to examine it from the point of view of the American psychoanalyst and group therapist Irvin Yalom's Ten Curative Factors of groups. This is his list:

1. Imparting of information
2. Installation of hope
3. Universality
4. Altruism
5. Corrective recapitulation of primary family group
6. Development of socialisation techniques

7. Imitative behaviour
8. Interpersonal learning
9. Group cohesion
10. Catharsis

1. *Imparting of information.* The information imparted during this session is very personal and on an unusual level but it is important to those who impart it that it is accepted and that other people try to understand it and compare it with their own feelings and experiences.

2. *Installation of hope.* This is an important factor in this session. Because patients are mutually supportive, they feel freer to express the very depths of their despair.

3. *Universality.* It is some comfort to patients to find that others have their problem and have perhaps begun to come to terms with it.

4. *Altruism.* This is mainly expressed by a more caring attitude to others outside the session. It is also a good sign when patients begin to help the therapists to move the chairs back into the room at the end of the session.

5. *Corrective recapitulation of primary family group.* Attendance on the short-stay wards, from whence these patients come, is too unstable for this to have its full effect.

6. *Development of socialising techniques.* This is not really that kind of group but it does give a realisation of another kind of communication than that of common politeness, trivialities and complaints.

7. *Imitative behaviour.* Patterns of attentive listening, serious thought and comment are copied. Many patients at first copy the movement of others and then discover their own individual body expression.

8. *Interpersonal learning.* A lot of helpful comparing and discussing comes up during these sessions.

9. *Group cohesion.* See no. 5, but within the groups a very good feeling of unity of direction develops from time to time.

10. *Catharsis.* This is one of the most valuable features of this group. In the warmth of the atmosphere the problem ripens. The patient seizes the appropriate moment to release her emotional explosion and allows the group to contain her and her personally uncontainable distress. The group's acceptance of this outburst is tremendously reassuring.

It could be asked whether patients would not do better performing structured group dances together. There is certainly a place for this in evening classes when they go home and in ward socials with occupational therapists. However, the orientation in this session is to work on oneself within a group and become able to tolerate, trust and speak about one's own real experiences. Through moving and speaking and relaxing to music one learns to relax different kinds of tension. To learn to be aware of tense shoulders and thighs, and of feelings of anger and jealousy, and to investigate their causes and try to do something about them – all this is every bit as useful to a patient who is going back to live alone and work in an office, as knowing how to do the Highland Fling and Eightsome reel just in case seven Scots and a bagpipe player should suddenly turn up.

Interpersonal communication is valued and stressed, most often to someone who is outside the group. The words repeated most often by the therapist in this session are: "Have you told her/him that?"

INCIDENTS

One of the incidents that I remember best was with Lena. She was in her late teens, a peculiar girl whose rather vacant, clumsy appearance was the outer casing for an inner music which produced some most sensitive and moving poetry. I first began to be able to see through this casing after she had let me read some of her poems. It was Lena's turn to choose from the pairs of Emotional Opposites. She took the two cards marked Accept and Reject. I can see her now sitting with the Reject card in her hand huddled up on the divan with the other patients. "It's me," she said bitterly. "A reject! That's what I am. Just like a cup in a factory that's no good." Out came a tragic – albeit one-sided – tale of not being wanted by father or mother or brother, of losing jobs, and being locked out at night and refused entry to hospitals. When the music began, we danced, and Lena put her head on her knees and her arms hung down and she cried and she cried and she cried. I sat with my arm round her shoulders and at last we understood through the sobs that she was about to go for an interview at another hospital nearer to her home. "And if *they* reject me, I'm *finished*," and she broke down again. Time was getting short. What could I say? "Lena," I said, "it is terrible to feel that your mother and father and brother and employers and even hospitals reject you. But it is not that which really matters. There is only one person that must never reject you." She looked up. "And that is you, yourself." Startled, she wiped her face.

84

At the next session her friends told me that she had gone off to the interview with a Psychiatric Social Worker, looking like "a million dollars". She came back radiant and wreathed in smiles having been accepted. Later she wrote from the other hospital saying that she had felt a bit lost at first but that now at last she really felt accepted.

This is an example of how a potentially restrictive dance title – a quotation from the work of Hazrat Inayat Khan, the Persian Sufi poet – brought out strong feelings about three different women's problems. Inge, a depressed married woman in her thirties with two daughters, chose "To love is one thing, to own another". Being in hospital, she felt that she was no longer owned by her family and this brought tears. Annabelle, a separated woman in her early forties with a grown-up son, realised that she was trying to own her only son and she cried bitterly. Linda, a young woman in her twenties, felt that her mother had tried to own her. Feelings about this were danced and the ensuing talk was so eager and the learning between the women so interesting that we never managed to relax at all and were seven minutes late on the next ward.

Another time Barbara chose "Volcano" from the seven conditions of fire cards. A middle-aged manic-depressive patient with a large family, Barbara danced the fire of her illness, flapping her red coat as the flames and then lying as dead – killed – on the ground. Inge, who felt her illness had disrupted the family, said that she was the volcano. Edna, a depressed and anxious woman in her fifties, felt that she was capable of being an angry volcano but when she heard the music (which was superb) she felt like a victim, as did Jean, who was also depressed. This brought up some interesting talks about anger and persecutors and victims which was all the more valid for having first been experienced emotionally and through their expressive movement.

At one session a large, bearded schizophrenic young man looked in my kaleidoscope to give us his vision as stimulus and he astounded me by saying, "I see God." Thinking – possibly quite misguidedly – that this might be an unsuitable stimulus, I asked irrationally, "What ELSE can you see?" He answered, "A garden." Patients freely fill the structure of this session with anything that is meaningful to them at the present. The therapist creates this emptiness by his willing receptivity.

OTHER OBSERVATIONS

During the movement, the therapist will observe interesting areas of rigidity in the bodies of the dancers which usually correspond to regions of inhibition of feeling and thought. Some people scarcely move their legs, some never raise their arms above their shoulders, some remain rigid between their shoulders and thighs, some only move in stereotyped dance steps, others insist on going round the room contrary to the direction of the rest of the group. Certain peculiarities can be commented on, others are better watched until their meaning becomes clear or until they are dropped as unsuitable end-gaining processes. It is better that the patient should gain insight that she can use of her own accord, tardily, than that the therapist should speak too soon and burden her with unacceptable and incomprehensible information, a defensive attitude and the feeling of being inadequate.

10. The small improvisation group, vocal group and record session

Between the intensive tuning of the individual session and the attempted all-inclusive resonation of the ward session, there are many possible music therapy treatment structures. These vary in the active physical, emotional and mental involvement that is required of the participants, and these variations can be very useful. Thus Mr B., 19, who is acting out his rebellion against his father in every situation where he finds himself under authority, can easily be contained in the small improvisation group protesting wildly on drums and cymbal and accepted as a spirited percussion player, while he would be a thorough nuisance in the vocal group or a record session. On the other hand timid, anxious Miss F. has not got the ego strength nor the desire to enter into her emotional depths during her short stay in hospital, so the improvisation group and psychodynamic movement are rejected in favour of the reassuring leader-centred vocal group where conformity brings harmony and beauty, and all emotion expressed is shared and contained within a formal musical composition with a safe beginning, middle and end.

THE SMALL IMPROVISATION GROUP
This kind of group is for patients or clients willing to attempt to clothe their feelings in the form of individually created sound patterns, to allow others in the group to do the same and to explore these feelings and their interrelationships subsequently in words. It is especially suitable for neurotic clients, those in need of help with relationships or self-expression and people whose identification with their rigid persona (role-mask) has made deeper expression impossible. It can be useful for borderline psychotics but these would probably do better in a one-to-one session.

What particular benefits are there in having group rather than individual music therapy?
Certain feelings come more easily to the surface within a group. First of all the feeling of being completely contained and accepted

within a group, which might take up to twelve or more group psychotherapy sessions, is available immediately in the musical group. Through the musical expression the members are united at a pre-verbal depth of consciousness. This might be the equivalent mental state to Freud's oral phase of sexual development but it can, I believe, go back to a foetal stage of total immersion and inclusion in a being greater than oneself. This can be an extremely releasing (from the responsibility of having to be an individual), revitalising and reassuring experience, like being dipped in a sea of collective consciousness and being enriched by it while yourself enriching it. A few people find it threatening and fear a permanent loss of ego.

Secondly, there is the experience of being able to hang on to one's own individuality in sound expression and – throwing oneself into the sound – blot out all other music in triumphant awareness of one's own. The discovery of the group as not-self and of how this can be excluded by powerful individual expression is a phase of useful and essential rebellion. This might correspond to Freud's anal phase. In this phase there is a sado-masochistic "either/or" feeling about aggression. It is "kill or be killed". One is either almighty parent or helpless child. I know of few other ways in which the full intensity of these powerful feelings may be safely experienced in a group. The realisation of the group's survival and acceptance of the aggressive attacks and the group's bearing the individual up over any despairing, helpless feelings following this, can make a very powerful impression on her. The original anal phase should be experienced at toddler stage. Most important is that the delayed acting out of this state of feeling, with its original all-engulfing ferocity, would, in adult life, almost certainly be extremely damaging to the individual or her environment. Having had the prototypal experience within the group, there is some hope that she will be emboldened to rebel more manageably in those external circumstances that require this response. Passing this stage successfully enables her to use her own will, without guilt, to make things happen and get things done.

Thirdly, there are the experiences of jealousy upon being excluded or rejected by other members who are relating to one another in sound, of having the choice of whom to relate to and whom to exclude within the group, and of the playful, flirtatious, truly responding pairing relationship between two equal partners without rigid dominance or submission on either side. This might be equated with Freud's genital phase. For some people, these experiences are almost impossible to work through in an individual session.

Within the group, players may show non-adaptive responses at different developmental stages which have not been transcended in life and these can be useful starting points for discussion. Only a whole person can truly relate to another. Before this stage has been reached the client is relating to projected self parts and experiencing a greater feeling of wholeness as she regains some of their energy. This is often felt to be less threatening within a group.

The structure

Numbers should be from four, including the therapist, to eight. If there are too many members and not enough time for each one to speak as well as play, the ones that are less bold will either lose interest or else suffer from frustration and possibly subsequently act out inconveniently in the environment. It is quite possible to run a group of three but it is a number which inevitably produces feelings of jealousy and exclusion and needs careful handling. However, good results have been obtained by exploiting just these difficulties, letting two of the members improvise on melodic instruments as the two partners and an excluded third play a percussion instrument. It can be very enlightening to discuss the relation of the feelings experienced to outside situations having the same effect.

The group should sit round in a circle, as far as possible. If the pianist cannot see the whole group, he can at least have the instrumentalists on either side of him. Melodic instruments might include a piano, xylophone and melodica, and percussion instruments could include side drums, bongos, tambourines and a cymbal on a stand. As many different tone colours as possible should be offered, to develop discrimination and add richness.

It is important for those who have never played before, that their playing should immediately become a meaningful sound expression and not merely an intellectual, physical and aesthetic activity. To this end it can be useful to resonate the group by immediately exploring in sound any problem brought up by a willing member.

In a group of teachers and piano students who were interested in gaining a more spontaneous approach to self-expression, Miss C., 20, a primary school teacher, began by talking about her inability to play in time. We spoke of the necessity of feeling rhythm as something coming from within rather than imposed from without and this led to Miss C. talking about feeling split between the impulse to enjoy pleasant but idle activities and the displeased side of her which felt that she should be committed to community welfare and other such serious pursuits. I suggested that we explore this musically. Miss C. sat at the xylophone with permission to be nothing but the impulse while the rest of the group played disapproving parental voices on percussion. It was, however, quite impossible for her to let go. She played a neat, measured little melody which was very hard to disapprove of and subsequently she expressed in words only feelings of apprehension about the impulse rather than any awareness of how it was when it was allowed to be. Next Miss U., 38, a head teacher, played the impulse. She was much freer but half-way through became aware of the parental band and started to retaliate on the gong in no uncertain terms. This was linked up with feelings of self-justification at being so free. Mrs R., 40, a piano teacher and seasoned performer, played away as the impulse in full flood, later speaking of "trying to blot out completely" all the parental voices. Mrs M., 46, a teacher, was also lost in the impulse but half-way through the improvisation had a vivid feeling that the parental band were the disapproving voices of her elder sisters. By this time the group was alive and Miss C. had now managed to be quite spontaneous and impulsive on the cymbal while safely held in the parental band.

The next improvisation was designed to unify the group in an archetypal idea. We played a spring with rain dropping down on to it trickling down into a brook then into a lake then into a river and on into the sea. There is no formal beginning or end to this type of improvisation. From the first note the individual's consciousness is held within the group. As Dr Foulkes writes: "The group tends to speak and react to a common theme as if it were a living entity expressing itself in different ways through different mouths. All contributions are variations on a single theme even though the group are not consciously aware of that theme and do not know what they are really talking about." I have found that this is not so clearly felt in a psychotherapy group but in a music therapy group it is a most powerful experience. One clearly feels the transpersonal musical message speak through one's music to the group, making the unconscious conscious. Miss C. was quite primordial with her cymbal clashes which I contained with rich, deep, broken piano chords. At the end of the improvisation it was clear that she had tapped her reservoir of the unexpressed. She told us how this had brought up in her mind an upsetting domestic situation where she had not expressed any anger and had thus allowed an untenable situation to develop. She was flushed and angry as she spoke about this, quite unlike the china-doll expression which she started with.

Wishing to encourage further physical and emotional involvement, I suggested that in the next improvisation on Wind, people would use their voices as a free instrument when they felt the musical situation required it.

We started pianissimo. The wind rattled and tapped. It scraped on the bamboo guiro and golden cymbal. The tambour boomed and the drum answered. Suddenly active hands were not enough. Mrs M. let out a tortured wail that was joined by Miss C. and Mrs R. Was Miss U. vocalising too? At the end it appeared that she was not; using her body directly to be spontaneously expressive was too threatening, she had cheated with an Indian flute. Mrs M. discovered that she could release reservoirs of great sadness in the wind's sound and she found it a very valuable experience being able to bring it out instead of letting it take her down inside herself so that she was alone with it. None of the others mentioned sadness.

The atmosphere in the room was totally changed following the session. There was a feeling of easy, relaxed communication, barriers of age and profession and hierarchy were swept aside in the unity of the emotional sound experience. The new members were somewhat surprised at themselves but pleasantly so.

If the group is unusually inhibited and unwilling to offer an emotional situation of their own as stimulus, it is possible to use a myth or fairytale for this purpose and let the group project their own feelings into it. Good reproductions of paintings, photos of geological specimens, flowers, birds or animals can be used to evoke responses from the group which can then be translated back into sound impressions. The therapist will watch out for fixed emotional patterns within the group. Does one member always finish the improvisation? Why does she need to feel in control of the termination? How does this carry over into life? Does one member always choose the loudest or softest instrument? Does another offer sforzando for sforzando in a forte passage and a third always back down or drop out? Who initiates and boils up the crescendos time after time? Who first reaches the climaxes? All these interesting patterns have their messages and meanings which are best left to the intuition of the therapist in charge. To attempt to give question and answer interpretation here would only bring us into the realms of *The Housemaids' Dream Book.*

What is the purpose of group improvisation music therapy?
The purpose of group improvisation music therapy is basically to achieve greater and truer self-knowledge through self-expression in sound within a group. It can be classified as a therapeutic group with a high rate of activity.

THE VOCAL GROUP
The vocal group offers one unique opportunity to those patients taking part – they can participate in an activity which, once a year at least, unifies representatives of the whole institution in which they live, cutting out all the hierarchical barriers and turning doctors, psychiatrists, secretaries, nurses, Sisters, Charge Nurses, chiropodists, gardeners, carpenters, physiotherapists, art therapists, music therapists, occupational therapists, electricians and patients into sopranos, altos, tenors and basses in a public performance of such an inspiring work as Handel's *Messiah* or Mendelssohn's *Elijah*. To long-stay patients, who enjoy little emotional excitement, the thrill of massed singing to an audience can be an event which makes life seem more purposeful and turns them into people to whom something also happens when they have visitors or go to visit relatives.

After such an event Mr Q., a schizophrenic patient who had been in hospital since he was eighteen – some seventeen years – said to Miss K., the senior music therapist who was conducting, "I never thought we'd do it but we did!" It was "we" not "them getting us to do it". He had attended rehearsals regularly except when his goldfish was dying. When it did die he returned and poured his sorrow into the music. He had thought that he would be too nervous at the performance but he sat next to an out-patient of the same therapist and reported, "I was all right with Bob beside me – I enjoyed it." A long-stay, depressive middle-aged lady who seldom spoke, said, "It was lovely, dear." A long-stay epileptic lady was full of expectation: "My sister is coming to hear us. I've told her she'll love it. She says I must wear my string of cultured pearls." Whoever cares what she wears on the other 364 days of the year?

The vocal group session lasts for one hour weekly. From the physical point of view the most obvious benefit is the improvement in breathing. Many people whose emotional disturbance is based on the feeling of having been rejected, retaliate by refusing to make a full exchange with the world by means of breathing. They snatch at the minimum amount of air with shallow chest breathing. As soon as they start to express themselves they let the world in, with deep breaths, later with sighs, laughter and singing.

This session demands real concentration, which has a sedative effect, and combines the elements of both work and play in a self-disciplinary but pleasurable setting where there is mutual support and responsibility. Songs, which are prepared for as polished a performance as possible, vary from simple folk tunes to part-songs, melodies with descants, oratorios and songs for solo and chorus. Once learnt, they provide opportunities for those who have little to give others, to create a little enjoyment around themselves.

Lastly, an important aspect of singing is its possibilities in rehabilitation. The singer who can join a choir in church, music club or evening class will be sure of the weekly support and companionship of one little group of people with similar tastes. This can do a great deal towards overcoming the feeling of alienation and loneliness that ex-psychiatric patients can experience on coming back into the community.

THE RECORD SESSION

A self-respecting music therapist should only introduce record sessions into his schedule where he particularly needs to use music to stimulate communication in a ward where there is no piano. This is the province shared with the musical psychiatrist, psychologist, nurse or occupational therapist. However, the trained music therapist will be likely to be much more sensitive in his choice of music and usually more aware of the possible emotional effects of that choice on his patients. Given an average open-plan short-stay ward with some alert patients eagerly awaiting discharge, others drugged senseless in their armchairs and the rest at some stage in between making restless peregrinations from the sitting area to the kitchen and lavatory, the therapist's aim might be to improve communication and to share himself and the experience of great music with the patients for one hour a week. If his attitude is receptive, tolerant and responsive, those who need his attention will be drawn to him. He should bring about six records to the session. Some of these may be requests from his former session. They may be increased by favourite pop records brought by one of the younger patients whom the therapist has invited to tell the group what he particularly likes about his choice before it is played. The therapist's six records should include various moods, for example serenity, sadness, gaiety and rhythm, nobility, storminess and reassurance.

On entering the ward the atmosphere should be noted. It is wise to enter into the prevailing mood – match melancholy with melancholy – then bring the mood over to something more central. Where there is one or more potentially aggressive patients, a piece of avant-garde music played quite briefly will often evoke a healthy flow of denunciation and promote more discussion than all the other records put together. Where there are very tense patients with arms and legs tightly crossed and chins pressed back and down, a rhythmic piece will release the tension through small semi-voluntary movements. This will be a good time to get such patients talking. Initially, a verbal exchange can be started by asking which of two composers the group would prefer to hear, perhaps asking if anyone has any strong feelings about them, passing round the record sleeve to any who are interested, and so on. When an excerpt has been played – and these should be short at first to prevent the music being used as a defence against communication – opinions, feelings, images and recollections can be shared. It is the quality of the therapist's receptivity that will bring out the patients' inner feelings rather than the particular questions which he asks. He must be willing to let things come up as they will. The last piece of music can be somewhat longer and at the end requests can be solicited from each patient in turn. This is a useful time to try to make contact with the withdrawn patients whom the music may have rendered more communicative.

Given a selected number of patients in a quiet, closed room, the group can be handled differently. Patients can be relaxed on the floor on rugs and asked to imagine a certain scene (such as a favourite holiday) to the music, afterwards discussing their different experiences. The prolonged positive use of the imagination – the opposite of worrying – is very much easier to the accompaniment of suitable music. For phobic patients, this can take the form of desensitisation exercises. For example, while the music plays, the agoraphobic patient will, in the first week, imagine standing on her doorstep, then, when she can do this in reality, walking to the nearest lamp post and so on in a hierarchical structure. The memory of the music is a positive reinforcing agent during the reality testing. These are just a few uses of the record session. Naturally a creative music therapist will invent a treatment structure to fit the need of his particular patients and the possibilities of the given environment.

11. Music club

The music club which I will describe here is held weekly in the music therapy room for one hour after tea. The room can hold about eighteen people if extra chairs are brought in and placed in two rows round the grand piano; it holds about eleven comfortably. It could perhaps be beneficially extended to one and a half hours, but the hour fits in with this particular time table and so this is the structure in which we work. Attendance is voluntary. Patients seldom come by referral from psychiatrists or other staff but they tell their friends about it or the music therapists pick out people who might enjoy it or benefit from it in their ward sessions. The result is that it is an ever-changing group with an invariably wide range of mental ability and emotional disturbance. For those to whom the hospital is home, it is the nearest thing to a musical evening in a friend's house that they will experience. For those who are soon leaving, it may be the first social occasion that they have had in months, due to the feeling of inner isolation which their illness has brought them. It acts as a rehearsal for going back into society.

IS IT AN ACTIVITY GROUP OR A THERAPEUTIC GROUP?
The main, unexpressed aim is for members to help to create and partake of a warm, receptive group atmosphere in which they feel that they can share their feelings, mainly through music, and be accepted. The music offers the opportunity to become a live, vibrating member of such a group and this is the therapeutic experience. The experience of belonging to a small group as a contributing member is important. This one hour out of 168 a week can be a seminal experience bearing fruit elsewhere. There are plenty of opportunities for being a non-contributing member of a group of 35 or more people on the wards. When a ward full of people sit all day long in straight rows and never relate, it can seem tidy, normal and creditably under control. (In fact, in some wards it seems to be the primary task of the staff to keep the patients tacitly sitting in these long rows and to prevent them from forming little conver-

sational units by moving their chairs into several circles. One elderly patient, herself an ex-Sister, said to me, "I'm not used to sitting down all day, I want to get up and look around and talk to people. They keep telling me to sit down. It is not normal." She solved the conflict by breaking her ankle.) However, the opportunity of being with only five to fifteen other patients in a warm and friendly atmosphere produces new expectations of relationship. In the smaller group in its confined space non-participation is recognised as being inappropriate behaviour.

RUNNING THE CLUB

Music therapists take turns to run the club, usually two at a time, one acting as leader and the other as assistant. Each one produces a slightly different atmosphere owing to their individual views and basic assumptions about the group. One will introduce more singing, one freer instrumental expression, another more discussion and the fourth more experimental improvisation and group expression. I can only describe my own method at this moment. I am sure it will change. One learns all the time. The music therapists never know who is coming on any one evening or how many there will be. Although there is a hard core membership of long-stay patients, the short-stay patients often only discover the club when they are just about to go home. One cannot plan from week to week and build something up, one can only improvise, receive creatively and nourish the shoots of individual expression and creativity that appear.

My first task is to create a group out of this strange conglomeration of mortals, a warm matrix of group awareness from which the individuals can safely emerge, be received and return to the anonymity of their ward lives increased in the dignity and stature of meaningfulness to themselves and others. I must do this knowing neither their diagnosis, their last role in society, their marital and family status, their orientation towards others or anything else other than what my eyes, ears and intuition tell me. It is not easy, but to stop and try to collect all these facts would be quite impossible.

In the beginning I take a very firm hold of the leadership role and push each member through the fears about being accepted, breaking their silence and revealing their inner music. Once this initiation is over I am less dominant and mainly responsive. Under this régime patients tend towards increasing initiative in fetching chairs, making room for newcomers, producing material for performance, bringing

new members, offering to share instruments and so on. They seem
to become aware of themselves as accepted, active components of
this group. So although this could be described as a dependency
group, it does not appear to make the patients more dependent in
the sense of lacking initiative and spontaneity. Rather the opposite.
At one time my colleague Miss V. experimented by letting any
patient who volunteered take over the leadership for a session, each
one knowing a week in advance that her turn was coming. The
gentle dignity and quiet control of some of the long-stay patients
was delightful to see. But none of them would attempt to initiate
any group musical activity apart from a little singing. They were
functioning on borrowed group awareness.

A SESSION

My colleagues are not with me today. Instead Ann and Johannes,
two music therapy trainees from the Guildhall School of Music and
Drama, have come along as part of their practical training. Ann plays
the violin and Johannes, who is from Germany, plays the piano.
Several patients are gathered in the music therapy room and more
enter as we put down our violins, get out the instruments and take
off our coats. As I take off mine, Eva, a girl of twenty-three, says,
"That's a nice coat. Can I try it on?" I let her do so. She flaps the
arms and shouts, "Now I'm the music therapist! Look, everyone!
I'm the music therapist!" "If you would like to be the music
therapist for tonight, you may, but I think you'll find the coat a bit
hot." "No, no. I couldn't. I didn't mean it," she says. "Is there
someone who would help Eva to take the music club tonight?"
There is a dark shaking of heads. Eva has not yet got the group's
trust. I would have protected some patients against this experience
but Eva is having individual music therapy and has somewhere to
take her wounds.

Everyone sits down. We are about fourteen people. I look round
and say, "There are two people I don't remember. Could we have
your names?" "Albert," a slim, pleasant-looking man in his
thirties replies. "Helen," a girl of twenty, who brought him, answers.
They sing but do not play any instrument, they say. "Everyone
plays here," says a long-stay patient. I give the names of the rest
of the members and introduce myself and the trainees. Everyone
uses their first names except myself and Mrs Ban. Mrs Ban is a long-
stay patient in her late sixties with a grey stubbly beard and the
typical pendulous breasts reaching her waist due to overweight,

drugs and having no bra to support them. She carries several hand-bags about with her, smokes as many cigarettes as friends will give her or as she can roll and has a few, lonely, monumental teeth whose final removal will at last put her in the running for full dentures and normal digestion. She speaks very little but sometimes responds unexpectedly and very much to the point. Her eyes, when she is looking outwards to the world, are warm and friendly. I do not know what using her surname means to her, possibly the same as using mine means to me, at any rate no one refuses us the right to cling to these possibly meaningful names.

Everyone is encouraged to take an instrument. There are bongos, side drums, maracas, hand bells and tambourines. I sit by the xylophone. "Now we all know each other's names and what we look like outside but I am going to suggest that we all share how we feel inside at this moment by each playing our feelings in sound patterns. I shall start." I feel rather comfortable and playful and fashion gentle glissandi up and down with a few diddly poms divided between the black and white keys. There are comments when I stop. "You sound happy." "You sound carefree."

As each person creates their sound introduction there is interested attention. This exercise tells the therapist a great deal about each member, her capacity for expression, her inhibitions, her sensitivity, and her areas of body immobility. It also gives the therapist the opportunity to comment on and question a patient about the meaning of a specially violent, or short, or long, or stereotyped emotional blocking type of playing. In my early days of music therapy I did not realise the importance of this and let go, unquestioned, a man who had given us the most violent expression on the drums. He went home at the weekend and went for his wife with a hatchet. Had he been able to tell us about the meaning of the violent feelings this might have been avoided. She was not harmed, as it happened, but it was a nasty shock for her. And for me.

Initiation rites concluded, we will perform as a group but we are a group of accepted individuals. "Johannes, would you improvise rhythmically for us to join in?" He starts with a tonal, sixteen-bar phrased piece of music and everyone is with him. He gradually loses the tonality and gets wilder and more emotional, his hands leaping up and down the keyboard, the tambourines barking at him like angry dogs. When we've finished we sit back and smile. There is a "That was Us" feeling. Marion, a long-stay patient with tremendous personality goes out and returns with a glass of water. "I can't sing today. I've got a sore throat. Doctor says I may have to have my tonsils out for the third time. They keep growing." I nod sagely. "Is that a xylophone?" Helen asks. I was waiting for someone to say that. "Yes, would you like to play it?" We exchange places and I take her maraca. "We'll make it a little concerto. We'll all try to play softer than Helen and in the same sort of mood." This is to be an atonal improvisation as she knows nothing about keys. "What are you going to call it?" "Morning," she answers. It seems like a really bad morning, this delicate young woman is furiously beating the notes and killing the sounds by keeping the beater down on the notes. "How did you feel about it?" I ask Helen when she has finished. "I wanted to make it sound angry." I explain how killing the notes actually makes less sound and how one can strike half-tone dissonances taking the beater away from the notes once struck and make effectively angrier sounds. At this point I do not investigate the cause of her anger as would be done in a small improvisation group. "Can I have a concerto now?" asks Eva. She presents herself as being far less intelligent than she is. Calling her piece "Vandals" she cleverly finds half-tone dissonances all over the instrument. "Did that sound angry?" "Sounded furious," growls Mrs Ban and the others respond with her. Albert has a turn. His playing is extremely sensitive.

Edith, a toothless, childlike long-stay patient, with her short white hair in a slide, rocks her sagging body, puts her chin in the air, shoots out her lips, and begins to sing a nursery rhyme in a husky treble voice. I go to the piano, find the key by good luck and put in a few tonic, dominant and subdominant chords. When we applaud she joins in. Edith seems to live in her child world oblivious of what is going on but nevertheless manages quite often to find her way right across the hospital to the music club at just this one hour during the whole week. It makes you wonder.

Ian, a tall, black-haired fellow in his thirties, gets up and announces, "I'm off to the pub now." "Have you time to sing us a song before you go?" He stands up grinning and muttering, "O Jesus . . ." and putting his chin up and eyes to the middle distance sings a song about "The Old Country Home", breaking down in verse two to enthusiastic applause. Mrs Ban gets up and shambles towards him with a thin, outstretched cigarette. "Can you give me a light?" she rumbles. "O, here's a decent cigarette for you, you old devil you." His face is wreathed in seraphic smiles. "No, a light," persists Mrs

Ban. "Now take it, you old bugger you, you know that's what you want." She takes it, smiles, sucks at it hungrily and returns to her place. They are good friends from the canteen.

"What have you brought, Oliver?" I ask. "Recorder? Mouth-organ? Songs?..." Oliver, a schizophrenic patient in his thirties, has been in hospital for twenty-odd years and makes good use of the music therapy department. "Actually, I'd rather play the piano," he says. He sits down, neck rather slanted forward, and plays two pieces by Mozart and Schubert with grace and order, involving as little of his body as possible. The body areas of immobility during performance are an interesting study both in hospital and on the concert platform. He smiles shyly at the applause. Where there is no pay cheque or promotion this is an important symbol of the community's appreciation of his efforts.

The door opens and Quentin, a man of fifty plus, comes in, greets the therapist angrily and some of the patients who make a chair available for him. A minute later, Marion announces loftily, "You will excuse us, Mrs Priestley, but Quentin and I are going to get married. We must go now," and the pair of them leave to a chorus of goodnights. Marion has a rich, shared fantasy life which combines with the nicest calculation of time and place as regards appearing where the hats and handbags and costume jewellery are being handed out. She is far too aware to want to live outside in the cruel world and adapts most creatively to institutionalised life, always being found outside where the action is although her ward is kept locked. Seen on the ward, typical chameleon, you would think that she was as incapable as the others. It is sad that so often psychiatrists spend their precious time with a patient taking infinite pains to discover the precise extent of their disabilities and abnormalities. Possibilities can go undiscovered.

Ann has brought a two-violin and piano arrangement of Handel's *Arrival of the Queen of Sheba*. Johannes, an ex-organist, brilliantly improvises the lost piano part, I play second and Anne plays first and everyone joins in on their percussion instruments. What a sound! One can almost see the procession. Faces are solemn but rather smug as they pound the instruments.

"Albert hasn't sung," says Helen. He sings with musicality and refinement from a book of folk songs which Johannes takes rather conscientiously at just the wrong speed. Somehow all the English songs manage to sound German. Should I intervene or leave it to Albert? I decide on the latter. "Who else has something for us?"

"I've got a poem," says Iris, a gentle, bulky long-stay patient whose occasional savage, self-destructive outbursts on the ward we can scarcely believe in. The drugs produce the typical restless repetitive movements in her limbs. "Is it your own composition?" "Yes, I wrote it on Saturday." She reads a fresh, lively verse about the awakening of nature in spring. This is a very hidden part of herself. I wish we knew it better. Another time we might have improvised music to it, line by line, but there is not time for that today.

James, a dignified elderly long-stay patient in his sixties gets to his feet saying he must go and do the tables for dinner. I am sorry I forgot to include him before as he often goes early. Bother. But one cannot remember everything.

"Could I play something, to finish up?" asks Zena. She is an ex-patient who comes back to help us in an unofficial capacity and is very useful on the wards. "I could play a duet, if Oliver would play bass." Oliver smiles his shy smile and they arrange the chairs. He would never issue the invitation. The little waltz finishes up the evening. There is applause. Goodnights. People help with putting back chairs and putting away instruments.

THE ATMOSPHERE

It is hard to give any feeling of the atmosphere by just describing what happens musically. Patients come in as lonely units from different wards or in furtive couples. They sit like ingredients waiting to be incorporated into one delicious dish. As the hour goes by the dish is made. There is increasing eye contact within the little circle, smiles across the room, little asides about music or performances and postures become more relaxed.

Sometimes critics have suggested that such a group could only be useful if patients arranged everything themselves. I do not agree with this. In society when one goes to, or gives, a party, there is a host or hostess who is responsible for the comfort of the guests. If one has never had the experience of being a cherished guest or cherishing hostess one is not likely within a single hour to be able to dream it up and produce it with thirteen emotionally disturbed strangers. People learn to love and accept by experiencing being loved and accepted and then desiring in their turn to give others this experience. Several of the long-stay patients have gone back to their wards and been instrumental in helping to run a party there with urgent calls for a music therapist to provide some music for singing or dancing. Many short-stay patients have remarked on the surprisingly friendly atmosphere that can be created without a drop of alcohol or any other drink among people who differ so widely.

OTHER INTRODUCTORY EXERCISES

As an introductory initiation exercise anything will do that will make each patient feel that her expression of her feelings is acceptable to the group. Games like giving the rhythm of their names or the rhythm of their favourite tune I find unsuitable at this juncture, as they are not expressive. A fixed title which everyone expresses in their own way such as My Happiest Holiday, My Bitterest Memory or What I Feel about Hospital can be very useful and the therapist can encourage quite a bit of discussion on the subject if he thinks that it will be helpful. An introductory exercise which I have found useful is The Unfriendly Chain. One person turns to her neighbour and plays very angry feelings (they are encouraged to look at one another), the neighbour plays submissively back to her then turns round to her other neighbour and repeats the angry salvo, and so on round the room. It releases a considerable amount of tension in the group through playing angrily and through laughter and each person has had a turn at being persecutor and persecuted while contained in a friendly group.

For the group expression, the heart-beat exercise described in Chapter 31 can be very effective. A book of paintings, or some paintings by patients in the group, can be used as the starting point for a group improvisation with volunteers playing the various aspects of the painting. Several short improvisations, with different patients (who will not be contributing much in other ways) being allowed to choose the stimulus painting, can also give scope for sharing the more interesting instruments.

During the introductory period the therapist will discover who is prepared to do what and mentally try to arrange for the more skilled performers to play later on so that beginners will not feel that too high a standard is demanded. The therapists should always play themselves, even if not invited to, as the live performance of skilled musicians in such a group does much to lift the atmosphere and raise the level of aspiration. The therapist needs, too, to remain a performer honouring the patients through his art. This also makes the patients feel more friendly towards the whole hospital as a caring community. Beautiful live music credits them with being spiritual as well as physical beings and caters for this special kind of hunger.

12. Therapeutic teaching and chamber music

NON-THERAPEUTIC TEACHING

In considering the nature of therapeutic teaching it is necessary to be aware of the sadly prevalent amount of damaging music-teaching that still takes place today. This is teaching which denies the creative, exploratory, expressive, generous and joyous approach to this art form and replaces it with a rigid, stale authoritarian approach experienced in an atmosphere of punitive greyness. For many of the pupils of the latter method, music has been a reason for being driven down the narrow alleyway of grade exams. They are unable to express themselves through music of their own choice, to fit their own particular little talents or weaknesses. Even today we therapists still meet the former piano pupils of teachers who have used that most primitive form of negative reinforcement: whacking the pupil's knuckles with a ruler when she played a wrong note.

What is the use of having the perfect, currently approved finger position if you are so afraid of losing it that you never play to friends, sightread from scores or play by ear? What is the certified ability to play all your scales and grade pieces correctly from memory compared with the enduring pleasure of being able to improvise or compose music – however fumbling – to express your own puzzling moods thirty years later?

The music therapist must care about such issues because he will have to pick up the pieces in his work.

WHAT IS THERAPEUTIC MUSIC TEACHING?

To the client it is a music lesson. She brings her music and instrument (if she is not a pianist) and she learns to play. But to the therapist it is different from a normal lesson, the priorities are altered. In an ordinary lesson the main purpose is that the pupil should learn to play as well as possible. In therapeutic teaching there are other aims which vary from client to client. To illustrate: Jean, 15, was extremely shy and unable to make relationships in school and outside. To her previous piano teacher this was regrettable but hardly his responsibility. Music was something that only increased her solitude. The music therapist, however, made Jean's ability to make relationships the main aim of the sessions. He allowed her to initiate conversation wherever possible and responded warmly, more to the manner than matter of her communication. Her piano playing, too, was experienced as a communication from her to him and discussed in this way. The choice of music was a kind of relationship. At first she chose pieces which she thought he wanted her to play. It was twenty-five sessions before she dared to suggest playing duets. One relationship being firmly established, he arranged that another pupil should perform the duets with her in the pupils' concert and she agreed to coach a third pupil in a piece that she had chosen and learnt previously. Gradually the ability to make friends grew with the musical life, and her playing improved, too.

Here is another example: a professional man in his forties was referred to me by a psychiatrist. He was a victim of obsessional neurosis, had had some minor brain surgery but was still very anxious and depressed. He had always loved music but his father had not regarded it as a suitable career. Now he felt that his music could never be reconciled with the rest of his life. He played the violin and it was agreed that he should have violin lessons. I decided to make his toleration, experience and expression of his feelings the main aim of our work. At first these were all fears, communicated verbally. The music seemed to be a split-off area of stolen delightful expression. Later on a lot of anger came up in speech. We were able to use this well to give firmness and resolution to Bach's *Violin Concerto* which he was studying. We discussed its use in his work situation and it went out into life again with good results. *Czardas* of Monti and an operatic selection were brought along and introduced as "My old enemies". We tackled them so that he should get the better of them and get the best out of them. I praised him for the growing expression and tone. I praised him for producing real music instead of rigid obsessional movements and sound patterns. I ignored monstrous misinterpretations of time values and poor intonation. "Why don't you mention my intonation?" he asked. "As you are aware that it needs attention, there is no necessity. You have a good ear and with your intelligence and education I know very well that you can work out the time values for yourself if you want to." He was loath to bring his calculating self into music but he did it. It was amazing how his playing improved. His obsessions diminished. In life, he became more adventurous, bought coloured shirts, went out and played his violin to little gatherings, and his work prospered. He no longer felt the impossible gulf between music and work, feelings and duty.

It is not an easy metamorphosis for a musician trained in the virtuoso class of a continental conservatoire to become a therapeutic teacher. The old temperament dies hard. Sometimes a little remnant in the therapist longs to fling violin, case, music and pupil into the corridor shouting, "Don't come back until you can count to four!" But gradually as one shifts emphasis from the music to the man one sees with delight that the music, too, has blossomed and developed.

WHY THERAPEUTIC TEACHING RATHER THAN ANALYTICAL MUSIC THERAPY?

In a psychiatric hospital many patients come and ask to learn to play an instrument. They feel that especially now, in their bewilderment and emotional pain, music would be valuable to them. But as they are mostly short-stay patients, there is no point in beginning a therapeutic teaching relationship and having it cut off after three weeks. We advise them to find a teacher when they go home and introduce them to the various music groups in the hospital and in its environment.

With the long-stay patient it is another matter. Therapeutic teaching is a valuable supportive therapy which will bring an element of pleasantly normal, non-medical activity into their lives. The warm, accepting relationship, the weekly effort to develop themselves through their playing, the talking point to share with others, the concerts with the excitement of the rehearsal and the other players waiting backstage, the applause as acceptance and appreciation of their effort, the shared party and feedback discussion afterwards – these are all enrichments of the quality of their lives.

In private practice it is different. If a client needs supportive care and also has a desire to learn something about music, the two needs can be met very well by therapeutic teaching. The client will not feel "abnormal" and in need of "treatment", she will think of herself as having music lessons and feel free to talk of them as such.

Clients with a very rigid personality structure, clients who have broken off an analysis because of an emotional crisis, clients who are not sufficiently motivated to try to change their life-style but are very dependent, these are some who can be taken for therapeutic teaching rather than analytical music therapy.

WHAT KINDS OF THERAPEUTIC TEACHING ARE THERE?

If a client is willing to sing or learn an instrument and has the possibility of practising, then vocal or instrumental teaching is the obvious answer. Doing is something that dispels doubts. To enjoy a skill and to give delight with it – even if it is only in playing incidental music to the local nursery school play – enriches life. But not all clients are players, some only want to learn about music. A session of listening to music and looking at scores and discussing form, tone colour and effects with relation to scoring and so on is a relaxing break in which quite a bit of therapeutic interaction can take place. A business man, as relaxation, had an hour of aural training, sightsinging, reading rhythm exercises on two drums with the therapist, improvising in pitch to set rhythms and singing to piano accompaniment.

I started a manic-depressive, Mrs G., 56, on composing for the first time in her life. She had a great deal of fun out of producing neat little eighteenth-century-style recorder tunes in four-bar phrases and discussing the pitch patterns after playing them through with me. Most clients, who would enjoy composing for fun, find that they can make a start by first producing a short poem and using the rise and fall of the voice to give them a lead as to how the melody might go. Even the most meagre attempts bring rich dividends in appreciating the creative process of the masters. A Mrs F., 35, used to organise improvisations with me. She would plan the story behind the sounds, decide which sounds would express which feelings, make a symbolic sketch and then record them with me and hear them back. She said that the exercise made her aware of the patterns of inter-action in her family life and she found that she had a more creative approach to a home life which she had previously found over-whelming and depressing.

If a client feels the need for the external authority's approval via exams, and finds them to be a motivating factor, then when she is well over the required standard, she can take them. But, if possible, the therapist should invent little concert situations as alternative motivation and encourage enjoyment and the self-appraisal of an internal examiner.

WHAT KIND OF MUSIC IS USEFUL FOR THERAPEUTIC TEACHING?

Music has special associations and meanings for different people, so I believe in using the music which the client really wants to listen to or play. Even to the extent of letting the client discover for herself that this music is much too difficult. She will then more happily accept the simpler music which the therapist offers. Side by side with her choice, the therapist will introduce his own choice which may be something which will develop much needed qualities of strength and firmness or bring out unrealised technical skills. Sometimes one can take the difficult music which the client wants to play and pick out little passages which are playable at her standard. The violinist, referred to earlier, learnt the second subject passages, the opening and part of the cadenza of Mendelssohn's *Violin Concerto*. To be "learning the Mendelssohn" was quite an event.

I believe that it is important for long-stay patients to play at least a little really great music. The inner activity of becoming attuned to it will make up for its possibly poor execution. This inner work is very important in the emotional climate of a psychiatric hospital. Unlike some of my colleagues, I believe that great music can tolerate a poor performance; it is bad music that must, at all costs, be played impeccably.

THERAPEUTIC CHAMBER MUSIC

As a rule the music therapist will have limited chances of running chamber music sessions and he should make the most of those that arise, however curious the combinations. Chamber music gives a group identity within the containing musical work. There is useful mutual dependency and support, each player is needed to carry out the task and the relationship is raised up to the level of the music being expressed. Although there is discipline, it is imposed by the music itself rather than by any external authority.

My first chamber music session was with a Mr V., 56, a violinist afflicted with alcoholism. He was very depressed and had a poor self-image. As we went in to a side room to rehearse Bach's *Double Violin Concerto* for a later performance, he said, "It is food for my soul. I never thought I would play this again." We began the beautiful, cool, falling melody of the slow movement and the hospital environment just faded out around us. We used his weekly hour to play and rehearse together, sometimes I was the pianist and sometimes the second violin. In the beginning his only talk was made up of orchestral jokes and stories, which his therapist relished having been out of an orchestra for eighteen years. Then he started handing me the treasures of his past life, moments of success given drip by drip between movements of Schubert's *D Major Sonatina*. We

107

began to arrange for Mr V. to accompany us on the wards playing his violin solos. His self-respect grew, his clothes seemed better cared for, he had an impeccable platform manner and was much beloved by the long-stay ladies in the geriatric wards. Now the verbal communication was changing. He seemed to want to practise being a teacher and the demonstrations of bowing techniques and fingerings gave him an excuse for the closer physical contact that he longed for, his home having broken up prior to his illness. It was only very much towards the end of his stay in hospital that he felt able to talk about his real fears and problems. He felt he was valued as a person now, weaknesses and all. It was a supportive hour. Unfortunately the environment did not co-operate in carrying on the support when he left. He was a candidate for the revolving door.

Another interesting session was with Mr B., 54, so depressed that he was almost mute. He was an office-worker who had played the organ professionally on Sundays and was a magnificent sight-reader. We used the session to run through any pieces that I had brought along to play on the wards together with any sonatas that I thought that he would enjoy. One week I remember going to fetch him and the Charge Nurse saying that he was so disturbed that he could not come. "Let him come," I said. "He is quite lucid when we play," and he came. That session he sightread perfectly, for the first time in his life, César Franck's *Violin Sonata*. It was not the free, expansive playing of a person who is in touch with his deepest feelings, but it was in time and with the soloist and the dynamics were correct and every note was there. And this was a patient whom the Charge Nurse found too confused even to speak coherently.

Music is said to stimulate the subdominant hemisphere of the brain, and perhaps in this way it calls up extraordinary forces in its service. In Mr B's case music was a substitute for speech, it was an island of sanity in a sea of desolation. But he used words more and more often as we worked. I would pretend to be tired in the middle of the session; we would sit down and drink coffee and he gradually brought out snippets of information about his external life. It was rather like having coffee with a sparrow. The fact that he did so well in his music therapy made the ward staff realise that they were not seeing the whole picture and they took this into account.

WHY DO CLIENTS WANT TO LEARN AN INSTRUMENT?
This is something about which a therapist must be rather careful.

On the face of it one might think that it was a generous, out-going, communicative, expressive gesture of wanting to discover delightful sounds in order to share them. Indeed, this is what the therapist must hold on to and work towards helping it to be. But he must realise that in many cases he is working against a powerful desire to build a little idealised region in which to escape from the harsh realities of life, a desire to repeat and perpetuate without development an earlier approving one-to-one situation with a favourite teacher or parent, or an excuse for withdrawing into endless solitary 'emotional masturbation' with no consequent sharing of feelings in human relationships in real life at all. In therapeutic teaching life's realities must usefully enter the session, music is learned to be enjoyed and shared with others, not hoarded away from the life-stream with its riches denied to others.

In therapy the social side of musical activities is stressed. The musical enthusiast can be welcomed and contained in a musical club, madrigal or recorder group, choir, evening class or amateur orchestra when she goes home from hospital. Because of the association with her therapist this can form a holding group in the community so that she will not wither away between the office and the bed-sitter. To be a music lover is to have mutual friends – Bach, Beethoven and Sibelius – with a great family of like-minded people. But to learn to enjoy their company and friendship takes patient rehearsal. If a person has not learnt to make relationships at three and a half, it is not too late to start again at sixty.

13. Working with art therapists and others

For a musician, working in hospital can be a lonely and desiccating experience. He may, therefore, find it enriching to share his work, problems, ideas, in regular meetings with the art therapists and possibly an interested psychotherapist whose work is at least as much of an art as a science. The three forms of expression: music, art and speech, have much in common and, in a sense, all three therapists use all three forms of expression while being most practised in their own. The psychotherapist, while mainly using words, builds up an inner picture of the patient's "ground" (in the *Gestalt* sense of the word) so that he can spot the missing "figure" and help her to complete the whole picture. He also listens sensitively to the music of the patient's feelings, the rhythms of speech, the deep tones of emotion, hollow, dry tones of defence and the recurring shape of the melody behind the words. The art therapist is also aware of the rhythm or halting action of the brush or pencil in his client's work and with his patient receptivity he catches the stumbling efforts to verbalise the seemingly inexpressible feelings evoked by the colours and forms which she creates. The music therapist needs a well developed faculty of visualisation both in the figure/ground use, in taking in and remembering the images described by his patients after their improvisations, and in mentally storing (in the form of some kind of primitive musical score) their musical creations. Words, he needs, too, to help the client to bring some semblance of her inmost feelings into the manageable everyday verbal exchange currency.

Like their musical colleagues, the art therapists regard the client dynamically. The client comes to them to create, and here creating means also *to be created*. Through doing this she is no longer just a patient – a victim of circumstances and a passive creature waiting to be actively cured by the trained experts – but she is also an "agent" taking a positive step towards accepting the responsibility for her own life and feelings. As Erich Fromm wrote in another context: "In order to grow out of the receptive into the productive orientation, he [man] must relate himself to the world artistically and not only philosophically or scientifically." Art forms a helpful bridge between the energy-sapping impossible cravings of the unsatisfied infant part of the adult.

The three expressive forms complement one another. Art relates most comfortably to the inert atavistic tendency holding the expression in a static form in two or three dimensions. In comparing a client's musical and artistic expression it is quite usual to find in art more emphasis on the defensive, structural aspect of the theme. Music exists in time and this allows for the dynamic changing process to be experienced through the force of a living emotional sound expression. Baynes says, "The atavistic tendency tends to hold psychic energy in the primordial, inert state where things are resistant to change. Harnessed to individual purpose, on the other hand, energy flows, increases and produces change. Psychologically, therefore, time can be viewed as a function of energy, for without the flow of the changing process there can be no sense of time."

Words act as a mental shorthand to express other kinds of experience and in order to get at the meaning behind them, the listener or reader is required to do a great deal of active translating work which may lead him to a totally wrong understanding of the underlying experience. There is more lying and misunderstanding when one uses words. But they have the mystery of flowing dynamically through time like music and yet being more static and binding in form than art. But just within these differences lies the power of the co-operation between these three kinds of therapy.

TRIOS OF COMPLEMENTARY EXPRESSION

One art form can, for certain clients, only be used to express a distinct group of feelings. Working in this medium the picture is incomplete. Thus, for Client *A* words are used to express only anger, disparagement and disappointment. This is her acquired habitual reaction to the outer world. Wonder, excitement and tenderness first reveal themselves in music. This is the denied hidden force of the inner world. Then again in painting a sturdiness, vitality of colour and the ability to carry an undertaking through make themselves known. This is the form-giving capacity at present being kept busy sustaining a wall to shut out the feelings behind the musical expression.

For Client *B* words are used for the expression of gentle, tender and appeasing emotions. Music is used for robust, angry and also yearning feelings, and only in the safe static form of art the chaotic urges of the instincts are allowed expression.

Client *C* uses words pedantically to bind force into manageable forms. Music he uses to express chaos and destruction with enormous terror and aggression, and art he uses for gentle experiments with organised change within a series of tentative forms.

CO-OPERATING WITH ART THERAPISTS

Music therapists working with guided imagery should always encourage their patients to express these in drawing or painting and then bring their work back to the music therapist so that he can see how the images have been developed. A young woman who described seeing her reflection in a pool in a meadow, went to the art therapy room and drew an interesting mandala picture with the pool and three pens full of animals arranged around a house in the centre. This restraining of the animal side of her nature was missing from the music. In our next session we examined the inside of the house, which was later painted, and she took one of the horses out of the pens and imagined riding into the forest and drew and painted this too. Such lively events are sometimes too threatening at the start of the work. With this very timid and repressed patient I began by asking her to improvise on four colours. She chose pink, blue, yellow and "horrible" green and later went along to the art department where she used these colours to produce a simple expression of forms in colour. Gradually we worked towards ideas having more emotional content.

Patients with chaotic emotions which seem to be attached to nothing but their body tension, can record a quarter of an hour or more of improvisation with the music therapist and later have this played to them as background music while they paint. This type of painting is usually full of movement and freedom, if a bit chaotic, and the realisation can be developed in tranquillity in subsequent paintings.

The art therapist may like to ask the music therapist to let one of his patients explore with music a certain recurrent feature of her painting – a volcano, a crescent moon, a sad bird, a menacing machine or the fact that she cannot finish any of them. Here the dynamic fourth-dimensional aspect of music may be able to do something to change the static form or pattern. As a result of this improvisation the discoveries can go back into a new series of paintings.

Using a stimulus expression from another modality is useful – such as painting to Bach or Stockhausen or improvising on a painting by Rembrandt or Klee, but it has a different function from exploring and developing the patient's own inner material through music and art. This may be the place to mention that opportunities for self-expression in music and art give rise to a healthy appetite for other people's artistic creations and there should be the opportunity to assuage this appetite with the works of the great masters wherever possible rather than the pseudo-nourishment of endless light music and illustrated magazines. A healthy balance between artistic intake and output helps to prevent emotional stagnation and indigestion.

CO-OPERATING WITH OCCUPATIONAL THERAPISTS

The occupational therapists can be a source of invaluable infor-mation as to the music therapist's patient's mental and emotional state during the whole week rather than in one intense hour of individual music therapy or group work. She will also have a clearer picture of the patient's day by day social exchange, dealings with external reality and management of such activities as shopping expeditions and inter-ward parties. It is worthwhile for the music therapist to form a good working relationship with these therapists and also to let them know his therapy times, he may otherwise find all his patients repeatedly spirited away to country outings, inter-ward table tennis rallies or swimming parties.

ATTITUDES OF PSYCHIATRISTS

The psychiatrists' approaches to the various art therapies vary very much. But three main types emerge. Some psychiatrists send all their patients to the industrial unit and forbid them to attend any kind of art therapy on the grounds that factory work is more in keeping with reality. Quite why putting tiddliwinks or cotton-wool swabs in plastic bags for six hours daily should be more real to a primary school teacher, double bass player or stage designer, than trying to create some kind of order in his or her inner life through artistic creation with the help of a trained therapist, I cannot understand. But then I have never tried it, and to an artist art *is* reality. Industrial training can do a great deal to steady certain individuals, especially if they are preparing to go on to this kind of job, but this work and that of the art and music therapists need by no means be mutually exclusive as successful results with patients attending both have proved. However, this type of psychiatrist appears to see all art only as some kind of seductive siren luring men from thoughts of honest toil in the factories, not as an industry in itself and a valuable enrichment to everyday life even when this may be spent in a factory. It is inadvisable to take on any patients from these psychiatrists because their patients are likely to be sensitive enough to feel the different approaches too keenly and this puts a great strain on all concerned. When new patients come unreferred to groups, it is advisable to ask who their doctors are so that one can sort out those who will be unlikely to profit from these therapies because of their therapists' different approaches.

One step up from this is the psychiatrist with a utilitarian approach to the art therapies. Sending six patients to art therapy he will say, "Teach them to do object drawing and shading, none of your Freudian nonsense", or "Teach this woman the piano, give her a cultural interest", despite the fact that she proves to be tone deaf, has no sense of rhythm and already has one overwhelming interest, in him. However, at least here there is communication and there are patients. The therapist should, however, bear the approach in mind when he returns any notes on the patient's progress.

The third type of psychiatrist somehow finds the time to tell the music or art therapist the patient's history and problems, answers any questions and asks the therapist if he can "do something for this patient". Such psychiatrists are people to be cherished because one can work reasonably with them and the patients will benefit from the good relationship. Brief notes about work done, material arising and observations on the patient's state of being can be returned weekly. These may lead to helpful suggestions such as "Try and sort out the sexual feelings from the aggression" or "Can you do some work on Mother?"

IMPRESSIONS OF A MEETING

This is a rough impression of a weekly working lunch in the Music Therapy room. Four music therapists Miss K., Miss V., Mr O. and I, three art therapists Mr G., Miss U. and Mrs A. and the Consultant Psychotherapist Dr W. sit in the small cane armchairs round a crowded coffee table, eating and talking. The patient under discussion, Helen, is being seen by Mr G. and Miss K.

Helen is thirty, single, has had a skin rash since puberty, which distresses her very much, and she spends a great deal of time in washing compulsively. A diagnosis described her as having a personality disorder with schizoid features and some depersonalisation. On meeting her one is aware of a pale, lank, apologetic person, difficult to relate to because part of her attention seems to be somewhere else wondering what other people's thoughts are about her rather than being at home within herself to greet them and find out. She is like a tall, sad, unwatered flower. Her paternal grandmother played a large part in her upbringing. Mr G. says, "Helen said she remembers her as always having a wet flannel in her hand and lunging at her to wipe her hands and face every time she touched anything." There were three younger siblings. The mother said grandmother had spoiled Helen.

Mr G. (shows some of her paintings). "I just asked her to paint how she felt in this one." It was a red question mark covering a foetus shape facing left in a dark green womb surrounded by a barrier with spikes facing outwards to the split colour background. "She was painting to Brahms' *Second Piano Concerto* which is unusual for her, she usually either only wants to listen or paints ignoring the music." The next was a solitary wash basin in a vast, unfinished bathroom. "She left it unfinished, she couldn't bear it." He had asked her to paint water in another context. A formidably glacial-looking waterfall was pouring down the side of a canyon. The earth looked much more fluid than the water. Tufts of green grass were at the bottom. "I asked her to try and 'feel' the water and she did and it felt less bad and she said she was more in touch with her body sensations but that it was a tremendous effort."

I was surprised at the range of expression shown in this drooping young woman's paintings.

Mr G. "I feel very helpless about this patient, she came to me the other day telling how she must be up at 6.30 a.m. to look after the old ladies in the geriatric wards and how depressing it is . . . they all want her cigarettes . . . she told me about her emotional pain and – what can I do? I feel that what such patients need are good experiences so that she can say 'No' to her bad internal grandmother. I felt her despair about herself. These patients can't have the deep relationships which I think they need. A lover for Helen or a warm mother for Bob [whom we had discussed last week]. I have no skill for dealing with their despair."

Miss K. "I feel the same about Helen. I can encourage her to work and do improvisations but I don't feel that it is altering her problem. I feel I must give her some hope."

Dr W. "You feel you must give her some help from inside you [indicating the waterfall picture]. As if her own water inside is drowning all her own good things. You are reflecting her wish for a fairy godmother to undo the bad grandmother."

Miss K. "There must be something alive inside her or she wouldn't be able to paint or write poems."

Mr G. "When she came in feeling so depressed and despairing all her painting ended in a rigid mess and she slid back into herself. Then I said, 'Don't run away from the emotion, do a drawing out

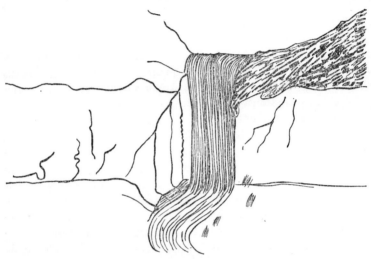

The waterfall picture
This patient's earth looked more fluid than the water

of that feeling of despair.' " He showed us a bold, coloured chalk drawing of a great green amoeba outside a red square cage which held a smaller purple amoeba holding a red cage holding the smallest black amoeba in the centre. "She was expressing her wish to explore and the caging grandmother and her wish to grow now and the caging hospital. She felt clearer when she had done it, she had made a strong statement and by using this feeling she had achieved something. There was some realisation that grandmother was not only outside in the past but a built-in part of herself, too."

Dr W. "Is there not something in this which can be fed back and interpreted to her so that she can be put in touch with her own internal resources? You feel that she needed a lover, but you can't be this, it wouldn't be helpful".

Mr G. "But I think these" (indicating amoebas in her picture) "are

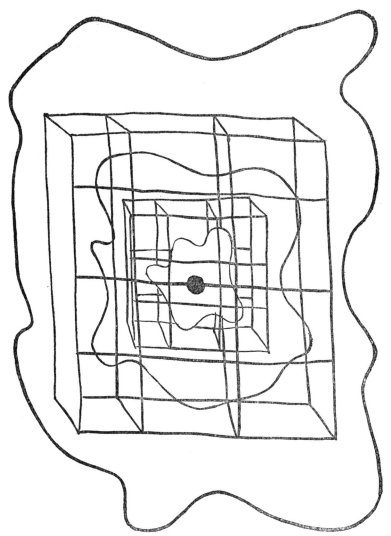

The amoebae and the cages

her growth processes – and these [indicating cages] her Granny
projections!"
Dr W. "Is she not saying in her despair that whatever structure you
provide she can overtrump it, swallow it up? What is it that feels so
hopeless? Can you find the human feelings which match the picture?
You have greater help than we psychotherapists have in your art

117

and music therapy, in such situations you have an added tool."

Mr O. "Have you used this picture in music?" to Miss K.

Miss K. "Helen brought it along and we discussed it. She talked about her fear of her skin and anything that touches it, saying, 'I suppose it all comes down to sex.' She said she couldn't feel her boundaries and therefore we inferred that she couldn't make contacts. She was afraid of attracting anyone too strongly, she said, so she kept all relationships at a distance and then was afraid of losing them altogether. We did an improvisation on the side of herself that she disliked, she described it as a 'shapeless lump' . . ."

M.P. "The amoeba?"

Miss K. "Possibly. Then we improvised as her rash versus the side with good qualities such as having a sense of humour even when gloomy, being good with children, having a vivid imagination and being creative with paint and sounds. We did a Splitting. She played her hated self with the rash first and rang the bell for the change of roles."

Miss V. "What did she feel about the other side – your music?"

Miss K. "She didn't notice what I was doing and agreed that she must therefore have become deeply involved with her expression. I said I found it difficult to keep a shapeless, formless improvisation going in the face of her good self music and I suggested that through her apparent shapelessness there seemed to run a strong thread of meaning."

Mrs A. "What did she say to that?"

Miss K. "She thought this possible but said that she must come to terms with it in her own way."

Miss V. "This seems to be a different view from that which Mr G. was given."

Dr W. "It is almost like the visual two-way perception in an alternating figure-ground drawing. What relationship have these structural squares got to the free but shapeless amoebas? There certainly seems to be lots of despair, looked at in one way . . . I was wondering if the idea of overcoming the cage (also implicit in the picture) has occurred to her. In her blinkered way of looking at it the cage is always frustrating the amoeba but the creative opposite is missed like a blindspot – the cage as the structure inside the amoeba."

M.P. "The shapeless lump being usefully inside the structure of the creative childminder with a sense of humour."

Dr W. "Hm. Patients tempt us to identify with their systems."

Mr G. "Never in her life has she experienced herself as an organic,

118

spontaneous being. There has always been this cage. Her psychic view of reality is limited and thus her despair. The idea of a closed structure might be the wrong way round but she *has* to see the cage as an enclosing thing – perhaps she's using it, she *can't* be the cage."

Dr W. "If the cage is the Super-Ego there will never be peace by getting rid of it. If it is cut off then comes the pay-off. She might try and forget it like drug addicts and alcoholics obtaining immediate relief. But then comes the pay-off – the psychosis, the hangover or the come-down. Conversely, if the amoeba were let out the Id would be too much. We all need to have our boundaries drawn in any game. Your difficulty comes about because you share and are restricted by her imaginings. The aim of music, art and psychotherapy is an enlarging of previous constriction and being in touch with parts of the self which, if released, would lead to other conclusions."

Mr G. "Then I'd have to deny her experiences to find the other way."

Dr W. "She might not have described them properly. Primary process thinking has about it the factor of condensation – of one story having several meanings enclosed in it such as you get in dreams, parables, myths and some poetry. This is the expression of the unconscious. Secondary process thinking, which our educational system is based on, has the intellectual confinement of one meaning. This way would indeed exclude your way of looking at it but seen in the primary process way it can have both meanings and more."

Miss V. "If Helen doesn't want to deal with the difficulty she puts it in a cage."

Miss U. "She denies her own responsibility for containment or structure."

Dr W. "For her thesis you must find her antithesis, only by this is there the possibility of making the synthesis." (He peers at the drawing.) "Aren't these male and female shapes? From this viewpoint doesn't she always see her femininity in terms of a perpetual cage strangling the amoebas' creative penises?"

The ground is worked over from every angle and the cross-fertilisation of ideas prepared the way for a fresh approach. The words help to examine and clarify the issues but they also bind and obfuscate. I feel the need to get back to the refreshing truth of living, changing music. In words This is This. In art it is This and That. But in music it is neither This nor That but the wonder of a mysterious dynamic Becoming.

14. Techniques of analytical music therapy

WHAT ARE ANALYTICAL MUSIC THERAPY TECHNIQUES?
An analytical music therapy technique is a particular focus for emotional investigation through music which the therapist uses with a client. The emotional inner territory is so vast and chaotic that it can be a help to both client and therapist to let their minds create and hold a certain focal structure. These techniques can, of course, be used by ordinary music therapists but it may be more difficult for them to interpret their clients' unconscious symbolism without projecting unrealised parts of themselves on to it, and they will probably work more confidently by using the material at a more conscious and matter-of-fact level. Such techniques as are described in this chapter and the following two have been devised, or adapted, to answer necessities arising within genuine therapeutic situations. New situations will always arise and I trust that their demands will be met by the creativity of future analytical music therapists. Meanwhile these are most of the techniques in current use.

WHY SHOULD ONE TECHNIQUE BE USED RATHER THAN ANOTHER?
When he has experienced and experimented with all these techniques in his Intertherap training sessions, the analytical music therapist will begin to have the feeling of which technique is called for at any particular point in the therapy. Perhaps the client is blocked at a deeper level and needs to work with symbols, dreams and images; perhaps she needs help in loosening a conflict knot through the Splitting technique* or perhaps she needs to find out what internal fear is holding her back from taking her next step forward in reality with a Reality Rehearsal technique.† As the client talks, some kind of picture of her internal situation will develop in the therapist's mind. Something will cry out for investigation. If nothing does, then it might be the moment to see what is going on beneath the surface with one of the Guided Imagery techniques.

* For explanation see p. 123.
† For explanation see p. 137.

Techniques of analytical music therapy

This will depend on many factors: how affected the client is by her music, how much insight she can take, whether she is using words as a way of avoiding music, or music as a way of hiding from interpretation and discussion. Sometimes a whole session goes by without the therapist having been able to persuade the client to play a note and sometimes there will be four or five long improvisations with scarcely a word spoken. For the kind of client who spins out the first three-quarters of an hour with defensive chatter, an immediate free improvisation, lasting about ten minutes, is recommended. In this way the defence is by-passed, genuine emotion is expressed, the therapist has some idea of her true feelings and has something real to relate to during the next part of the session. As clients get to know the techniques, they often co-operate usefully by asking to explore a feeling, relationship, or problem area with a certain technique. Of course, they also sometimes do this to put off the moment when they have to tell the therapist the answer which they already know and are unhappy about facing. But by this time the therapeutic couple know one another.

THE HOLDING TECHNIQUE

This technique is also sometimes called "containing". Its purpose is to allow the client fully to experience her emotion right through to its climax through emotional sound expression while being held emotionally by the musical matrix of the therapist. It is the musical equivalent of the small child going through a tantrum, heartbroken sobbing or transports of wild delight while being safely and lovingly held and guarded by her parent. This diminishes the fear of disintegration under high emotional stress, gives the emotion the chance to evolve into something different, and dissipates enough bound energy to allow the client to think more and feel less about the subject.

The therapist must create a safe container for the client's expression by his music. It must not be a constricting container which forbids full expression. At no time should her expression exceed his so that she gets the feeling that she is having the burden of carrying him along. On the other hand his expression must not be so violent before she is ready to express her feelings as to shock her back into non-expression. If it is just right the client will probably be oblivious of it but if it is wrong she will be uneasy and feel "let down" or constricted. During conversation the therapist may be aware of the emotional possibilities of the matter to be investigated and, at the start, he will let the client lead, then be a little ahead in expression, urging her on to the height of the emotional experience. Having achieved this she may be fully contained but running wild in the situation unable to make the turn. His task then is gently to bring her back, and this is done by changing to tonal music and containing the frenzy in strong major common chords; then she can feel that her excitement has a place in the harmony of life and has in no way damaged the environment.

It is important for the therapist to cease playing the very moment the client does so and let her expression at once flow freely into words. Again the therapist is the container. This time the emotion will be expressed in a less dynamic and more concrete way and there may be an attempt to examine the reasons for the feelings after the experience has been clarified. If the mood being contained is one of sadness or mysterious peace, the client may want to remain silent. But the therapist's close attention and willing reception of this silence is also a kind of containment. He can turn an intending blocking silence into the most intimate shared experience by his receptivity and holding of the relatonship. Such moments can be most pregnant and fruitful for the client when she realises that her punitive act of withholding communication is not being reciprocated, that she is not blocked out of anything but, on the contrary, while lovingly held, is being allowed to reach down and bring something up out of herself, taking as much time as she needs to do this.

The musical containing experience can be extremely taxing to the therapist. It is unwise to undertake this if the therapist has not really been through the full gamut of his own passions. Even so I can remember one particular session which almost split my mind and left my limbs so shaky that I found it quite difficult to become sufficiently composed to play the violin on the ward which I had to go to afterwards. I may say that this was a peak violent experience for the client, too. After that session things were more manageable for both of us.

Example 1

A woman of 33 came to the session terribly tense and said she was rejecting her husband sexually and blocking out the words of the consultant psychotherapist in her group meeting. After four attempts which she foiled with conversational gambits, we improvised

"Rejection". She drummed with frenzied energy and determination for a long time only stopping when she had to gasp, "Gosh, my arms ache!" She was very much more relaxed following this and could then freely discuss who she felt had rejected her in the past.

Example 2

A woman of 32 talked about life being humdrum. We improvised "Everyday" and she played a brief piece in sad beats. We tried "Adventure" which was played rather timidly on a maraca, tambourine and drum but her vivid fantasy of having lots of money, new clothes, hair done every day and visits to *cafés dansants* was the start of a more adventurous real life pattern and at the same time she found more pleasure in mothering her children.

Example 3

A man of 33 in his second month of weekly therapy wanted to explore his feelings of hope and despair about his illness. Twice he let the hopeful feelings be overcome and then the two feelings went into a terrible battle and he felt sleepy and "dropped away". This sleepy feeling was his subsequent reaction to the emotional awareness of strong feelings in conflict in himself and in the following week he frequently felt the "dropping away" sensation but took courage from the knowledge that it was part of the battle for health.

THE SPLITTING TECHNIQUE

The splitting technique is especially useful where the client has projected part of herself on to another character and, in doing so, lost the emotion invested in this person. Let us take the example of Grace, a timid, well-brought-up young woman, unacquainted with her own deeper feelings, who unconsciously resents her landlady Mrs Plum's interference with her life. Not wanting to face her own anger she projects it on to Mrs Plum whose actions then become coloured by Grace's anger. Grace comes to treatment in terror of this woman. By improvising as herself (Grace) while the therapist plays angry Mrs Plum, and then playing Mrs Plum while the therapost plays the victimised Grace, Grace has a chance to get in touch with her own anger over the situation and, with its protection as a consciously owned force, Grace can come to feel less threatened by Mrs Plum, being now faced with this lady's real anger only and not her own projected unconscious anger ricocheting back at her as well. This is an oversimplified example as these things take time to work through and understand but perhaps it will explain the principle behind this technique.

Another use of this technique is for conflict situations where all the energy is being held in maintaining the status quo and nothing appears to be happening, but at the same time the client is quite exhausted and has difficulty in getting anything done. In this version the client gives a word picture of her feelings about both sides of the conflict and then the music therapist starts off rigorously in the character of one person or idea. After a time it is useful to let the music become a duet, a mixing together of these opposed forces. Where the client breaks off before this point, a third improvisation can be done having both titles and being carried out more on the lines of a Holding technique.

Example 1

Barbara is a young wife and mother with obsessional traits. She has a violent fear and hatred of her sister Rose. I played her civilised self and she played Rose with tremendous excitement and energy. Then I was the wild, uncontrollable Rose and she played a two-semi-quaver and a quaver ostinato with a sforzando when she could hardly bear the excitement. Barbara could hardly resist joining my wild Rose music. Following this session she gradually began to own her own wild feelings about Rose and resist her intrusions in reality – a little unmanageably at first. Her tight, doll-like expression relaxed and she was able for the first time to show affection to her little daughter who had the same hair colouring as Rose.

Example 2

A young office worker, Thelma had troubles over suicidal feelings. We were splitting "Chaos" and "Punishment". It was difficult to work with Thelma as she always wanted to break off relationships, life, therapy. I played "Chaos" very wildly, she rattled a maraca a little as "Punishment" and then stopped and somehow mentally froze me out. It was impossible to continue playing. She succeeded in giving me the breaking off feeling completely. This session was followed by her repeating the experience within a sexual relationship. She just got out of bed and walked out of her boy-friend's flat in the middle of the night after engaging in sexual intercourse without herself experiencing orgasm. Our subsequent examination of her fear of any kind of natural or emotional climax was very useful.

Example 3

Thelma again, prior to going abroad to work, had mixed feelings about leaving her unenthusiastic widowed mother and was frightened that her own enthusiasm would suddenly vanish. She played herself as being sad while I played "Bright Mother" and Thelma's music got more and more angry. Then I was "Sad Mother" and she was "Enthusiastic Thelma". The mother's sadness made her feel guilty, so much so that she stopped. This was the danger then. By thinking the whole idea through and making a plan of action she gained enough confidence to keep up her enthusiasm and carry out her plan.

Example 4

A university student, Eva, wanted to explore with me her unequal relationship experiences. I started by being "Doormat" while she played "Dominant" but she was not concentrating on her own expression but trying to provoke me all the time and she said that she thought that if I did last out then she would have to be "Doormat". Next I was "Doormat" but I left spaces for her to answer back musically but she never did. Next I made a long decrescendo to see when she would dare to reverse roles. At my pp she was ppp and then when I reached ppp suddenly, right at the end, she did assert herself. Following this, she felt able to resist her tutor's efforts to make her take up work at a "suitable" school whose principles she disbelieved in, and to risk looking for a position in which she would feel happy and honest.

INVESTIGATION OF EMOTIONAL INVESTMENT

This technique is used in cases where words seem to lead you round and round in a circle and you get nowhere. I have found it a very good method of comparing a client's feelings about the marriage partner and another person who has become irresistibly attractive. The client and therapist together improvise with the title of the two characters one after the other, the therapist using the Holding technique. But here the therapist is also a very sensitive accompanist and most of all a listener. He should not give way to any counter-transference feelings at all, only accompany the phenomenal sounds and then listen to what is said about the two characters and compare this with the sound pictures. It is best not to play back this recording to the client as she will be very defended against the truth at this stage, but it can be taken as the basis of work in the future. This technique can also be useful when a little verbal phrase pops up again and again obviously loaded with special meaning and emotion. In this case the therapist will use counter-transference feelings as in the Holding technique.

Example 1

Beryl was a young wife with two children; her marriage had deteriorated until it was a sharing of child rearing, home and money. But she had met Oliver, an older man who doted on her, visited her daily in hospital (unlike her husband), idealised her, wrote her romantic letters telling her that he would wait until her children were grown up. He was totally undemanding sexually. The improvisation on Oliver showed a very rhythmic, gentle feeling almost like rocking a cradle. The improvisation on the husband was arhythmic, dynamic with many different kinds of expression. I put my money on the legal relationship. The next week, on an impulse, Beryl went out to visit Oliver without warning and found him in bed with another woman. The marriage took a turn for the better. Here her words had convinced me that her marriage was dead and Oliver a kind, unselfish possible replacement. But her music said otherwise.

Example 2

Kathleen, 33, with three children, was wildly in love with Ian and unable to have any feelings for her husband but those of a child. We improvised "Affair" but there was not much emotional engagement. When we played "Marriage" (meaning her present marriage) there was much more depth, a feeling of contentment which she said was in the marriage and with the children. Kathleen battled through all these feelings, another woman conveniently went off with Ian, and she and her husband subsequently came to a much better understanding. Later, this woman having abandoned Ian, Kathleen had a very brief affair with him but returned with a deeper commitment to her husband.

Example 3

Vera, 30, was complaining of her fear of travelling in buses, especially waiting at the stops. We improvised "Waiting", the music was rather subdued but played on every instrument there. Her inner experience was of waiting, being faint, getting on the bus, fainting, not being able to visit mother but having to be taken back to her husband. This led to several sessions of sorting out feelings about her father and husband. Some time later she was coming to the sessions quite confidently by bus.

ENTERING INTO SOMATIC COMMUNICATION

Sometimes physical symptoms are messages telling you that you have wrenched a muscle and must be careful how you move; sometimes they are communications about emotion which has been by-passed by conscious experience – "organ-jargon". In the latter case they can be stubbornly resistant to the usually helpful remedies. If the client can let the therapist play "Her" while she fully puts herself into being the symptoms, she can often get in touch with the by-passed emotion and, because of the tension released in the music, allow herself to experience it. When she does it may be very painful indeed. Such mechanisms are not in use for nothing. But what one experiences one can talk about, think about and work on; when the emotion is hidden one is helpless. Sometimes, too, genuinely organic symptoms are also the carriers of communications about by-passed feelings and this can make them more difficult to tolerate and to treat.

Example 1 (see Example 3, p. 126)

Vera, 30, came to her session looking rather depressed. She had a severe headache following a row with her husband. She played the "Headache" and I was her, it was a nice bit of chamber music. During this music she felt very angry indeed. Then we reversed it and she was herself as patient victim, feeling just the headache. She had a great deal of guilt about her aggression and if she expressed any she always turned the residue against herself. Earlier this had been expressed by taking overdoses of sleeping pills; the headaches were, in this case and in many others, a beginning of being able to contain and transmute these feelings more constructively.

Example 2

Ian, 32, was having trouble coping with his partially released aggression and was sometimes experiencing pains in his neck and shoulders and a "wandering" feeling in his head. On being the "Wandering", he played with tremendous force, hammering the xylophone keys till they leapt off their pegs and then when he heard the playback he found that he got the pains and his hands were gripping the divan where he lay, the knuckles white with tension. He subsequently adopted a more interested, experimental approach to his various symptoms, not feeling so much of a helpless victim, and a short while later, without outside coercion, willingly took on more challenging work.

All the clients and patients in these examples were coming for music therapy sessions over a period of time for quite serious disturbances. These were not one-session treatments.

With regard to the patients in hospital no one can be sure whether it is the chemotherapy, group psychotherapy, individual psychotherapy, art therapy, music therapy, occupational therapy, industrial therapy, the fellow patients, the nursing, the cooking, the chaplain, time the healer, or what that helps most. I find it a good rule to warmly congratulate all my colleagues for any successes with mutual patients which I think that I may have helped with. What one sees in one's own sessions one is sure about but it is only part of the whole picture that reveals itself when the team meet. Everyone has a part to play and no one should be made to feel unimportant.

15. More techniques of analytical music therapy

The techniques described in Chapter 14 were all suitable for investigating conditions of which both the therapist and client were fully aware. They are perhaps the easiest for the lay reader to understand but they are not by any means the first techniques to be applied in treatment. Too often clients present the conscious mind in a state of painful aridity, due to the lack of any creative and fruitful relationship with the unconscious. They never dream, they say, or if they do their dreams are quite meaningless and immediately forgotten. The inner geography is a stony, pessimistic desert, the season a perpetual winter. Their outer life reflects this picture. This is the time for using symbols.

Symbols are accumulators and transformers of psychic energy. They have the relationship to ideas and action that an iceberg has to a waterfall. Using them, the therapist is dealing with the transformation of force. Normally this can be very tricky but the music therapist has this unique lightning conductor: the tapping off of the surplus emotional dynamism through shared sound expression. It is not the psychic energy that turns to glowing cheeks, shining eyes, humming nerves through the body, and laughter, passion or tears, that is dangerous. It is the cold, frantic denial of emotion that causes horrible splits in the mind and leaks out into strange ideas, bodiless voices and chill moonlit inner landscapes.

At the beginning of treatment then, there is often this need for a loosening-up process whereby the unconscious can be allowed to fertilise the conscious mind. At this time the client's symbols will tell the therapist the things which she cannot herself say, simply because she is not aware of them. But once expressed and experienced they have an effect on her. They have their own most convincing reality which is often felt to add a richness and an added dimension to an otherwise sterile inner life. They also have a purpose in outer reality, and it is the therapist's task to create a bridge from the manifest symbol to its meaningful expression in outer reality. If this is not done the client can get drawn inwards – almost like a drug addict is – enjoying the images but shrugging off all responsibility as to the meaning and purpose of their translation into everyday life and work and endeavour. In this way, far from transmuting her energy into her individual conscious life, her little remaining energy will seep back into the inner life to try to find satisfaction there. For this reason the analytical music therapist will encourage clients working with symbols to "earth" – or concretise – the energy through as many modalities as possible. For example, first will come the inner realisation accompanied by the musical expression. This will be followed by a description of the symbol in words with details about the client's feelings and physical sensations experienced during the musical expression. Then the client may draw with coloured crayons or paint – however crudely – the symbol when she gets home and once again different attributes and meanings will be discovered. These may then be the basis for another musical investigation at a more conscious level. In this way the energy will be safely transformed and all the time the meaning for outer life will be discussed.

Two kinds of client are very difficult to work with in this way. One is the very extraverted client who cannot see beneath the surface of anything and has no awareness of the noumenal side of life. If her defences can be gently eased she may benefit greatly from the use of these techniques. The other is the client who is too introverted and needs firmer hold on reality through a well-made bridge from unconscious to conscious and the growing willingness to be responsible for the outer expression, through sound expression of inner realisations. The immediate tapping off of the emotion through sound expression held in the therapist's music greatly reduces any possible danger of "flooding" by the unconscious. Music therapists vary in their ability to enable clients to realise these inner images and what one client can experience with one therapist she may be quite unable to experience with another.

GUIDED IMAGERY

These techniques have been adapted from some examples given in Dr Roberto Assagioli's book *Psychosynthesis*. The first three are very useful early on in treatment and the fourth can be useful throughout. The client should be told what scene to conjure up but not to think about what will happen. "Just see the scene and start playing, let anything happen but keep contact with me through your sound expression," is roughly what she is told. Some clients find it hard to visualise anything at all before their music has reduced some of their emotional pressure. They can be given a preliminary Holding exercise on Anxiety or Fear to reduce tension. Others have a very impressive experience and break off in fright. They should be encouraged to go back to the scene and come to some kind of conclusion. This is usually reassuring to them. The therapist's musical technique will be as in Holding and his counter-transference expression can be of the greatest possible assistance to the client's inner realisations.

THE CAVE MOUTH

The client imagines that she is standing hidden behind a tree in a forest clearing watching the mouth of a cave. As she watches, something emerges. The forms that emerge are usually symbolised projections of suppressed or undeveloped areas of the client's responsibility. They can be understood as pre-verbal images.

Example 1

A young woman of 32 with depressions, making a very feeble contribution in marital and maternal roles, improvised with lively music and experienced going into the cave, being attacked by bats, which she fought and then found a pirate's treasure of coins and jewels. Being encouraged to go back and get it out she experienced going to get help, bringing the treasure home and having a party. In her case the black bats of angry depression had prevented her from using her true inner wealth. The step of "going to get help" was a significant one which was later acted out in useful ways during her treatment period.

Example 2

A university student, with a feeling of a splitting between her inner and outer self, also entered a cave which was wet and cold and there was a "sinister lurking" feeling and a sensation that the walls would fall in. The music was very sensitive and expressive. This was, in her case, tied up with the fear of a kind of implosion with no protective affirmative radiation from a true centre of being. It gave an indication of how to proceed by setting out to help her to find, and play from, this centre.

Example 3

A young wife and mother with hysterical suicidal impulses saw a lion come out of the cave and she fought it again and again until at last her steady beat at the end showed that she had won. She slowly began to make the psychiatrists and other attackable persons into lions for fighting instead of turning all this feeling against herself. Later on situations to be conquered were lions.

ASCENDING A MOUNTAIN

In this technique the client imagines that she is climbing a mountain and is asked afterwards to report on such details as the climate, the terrain, the size of the mountain, view from the top if reached, her apparel and any obstacles in the way of the ascent. The mountain is the measure of aspiration in life and the obstacles inner or outer hindrances.

Example 1

A man of 49, a taxi-driver, showed little emotion in his playing. He said he saw the mountain, it wasn't more than a green hill really and he thought why should he bother to climb it anyway, he would go for a walk in the sunshine instead. This was typical of his attitude to life which was to try to get some fleeting sensual pleasure out of his days while life lasted, without regarding the cumulative results of his actions or other possible sources of satisfaction which might be more lasting. He was a very unhappy man under the mask of a happy-go-lucky fellow and grossly obese.

Example 2

A university student with identity problems felt expansion as she climbed to the top of an English mountain. We discussed why it was such a small one. She tried another, abroad. As she toiled up I experienced overwhelming depression by counter-transference and then she stopped and said she couldn't go on, it was grey and hard and cold and lonely. She spoke of her two siblings, one – whom she rather despised – who had settled for a safe, routine job, and the other, her ideal, who was so dedicated and earnest about his work that it seemed to leave no room for feelings and pleasant side alleys. We were able to look at other possible models and she subsequently adopted a much more creative and individual approach to her own career and talents.

Example 3

A young man of 29 had an immature personality. His playing was extremely sensitive, using the drum and cymbal at first alternately and then together with some excitement and with responsive musical interplay with the therapist. There was no feeling of form and it went on so long that finally I had to end it. He said that he had imagined himself toiling up a mountain with snow and blizzards raging all around him and then had just been lost in the music. His lone parent had died when he was 16 and he had lived with relatives and taken various jobs, but had broken them all off or been asked to leave through quarrelling with his work-mates. One could say that he had a life-pattern of losing his aspirational aim through getting lost in the music of the emotional interplay.

Example 4

A young woman with compulsive suicidal impulses did some of the most solid and rhythmic drumming that I had ever heard from her in climbing the mountain. She reached the top and said it was marvellous that she had struggled up there in spite of all her slipping back. This was a pattern of effort and achievement that we often looked back on through the next year of just that kind of progress.

THE POOL IN THE MEADOW

The client imagines that she enters a meadow and goes and looks into a pool in the far left corner to see what emerges or what she can see in the pool. This exercise usually shows disturbances in the sexual sphere in the form of repressive or regressive tendencies of the personality.

Example 1

A woman of 32, wife and mother, who was frigid, entered the meadow going past cows and horses and looked into the pool, on which there were ducks, and saw her own reflection which she said she disliked. This brought up some interesting discussion about this bad feeling concerning her image and how embarrassed she had been as a girl at the arrival of her ample bosom. Her painting of this scene led to further improvisations and pictures and there was a subsequent amelioration of her condition.

THE DOOR IN THE HIGH WALL

This technique aims at releasing, in pre-verbal imagery, symbols clustered round any idea which is felt to need investigation. The client imagines a long, high wall in which is a door marked with the matter of the enquiry, such as: "Fear", "Love", Why...". The client imagines that she goes through the door and notices what is on the other side. Sometimes out of the jumble of images a feeling of certainty and great peace emerges.

Example 1

A woman in her forties was experiencing very painful and time-resonating jealousy.* The door marked "Jealousy" turned into a bird cage with a green eagle's head pecking at its own throat and then a huge claw attacking its breast. The cage faded into green and blue clouds with sudden red points. ("Like nipples which can only feed one at a time," she said.) Then there was a veiled moon and a white flame. ("There is a feeling that the moon cannot accept the sun's light because of the green clouds.") She was asked to become the moon and said, "A beautiful, mysterious Venus was locked in the moon and she whispered a world of marvellous feminine secrets to me." As the bird, she said, "I was attacked instantly by terrible feelings in throat and chest while I played on the guiro and screamed raucously and then suddenly thought, 'That is what I am doing to X' (the object of the jealousy) and felt ashamed." She was profoundly moved by this experience and subsequently battled hard to let calm thought into this area of painful feelings and potentially spiteful action.

MYTHS

This is a technique which I have not found it necessary to use as yet in individual therapy. It is indicated where the client feels that directly personal imagery and emotion are in some way threatening. The therapist will read out a simplified version of a myth or fairy tale such as the legend of Orpheus or the story of Cinderella, and using the Holding technique they will improvise together, imagining each scene. The personal deviations from, and the details added to, the original story can be used fruitfully in discussion, and the musical expression and relationship will tell the therapist something about the feelings which the client so much wanted to hide from him.

INTRACOMMUNICATION

This is a method for working on dreams. All contents of normal dreams can be thought of as parts of the dreamer split off and put temporarily outside her awareness to be looked at. The therapist

* A time-resonating emotional experience is one which is loaded with a disproportionate amount of feeling from an event in the past, the impact of which was unexpressed or possibly unacknowledged at that time.

notes down the client's dream – or dream fragment – with each noun having a separate line and number. The client first gives associations to each item then enters them in turn and speaks as if she were they. Parts of the dream can then be improvised on and items which did not meet or confront one another in the dream can communicate as in the Splitting technique. The client is then encouraged to find the meaning of the dream for her real-life situation. Whether or not a person believes that dreams do have a purpose, the search for meaning is, in itself, a valuable exercise and brings up a great deal of useful material to work on.

Example 1

With a phobic woman of 38, wife, mother and part-time employee, I worked on the following dream during her second month of therapy. The associations are in brackets and the intracommunication in quotes. The dream went like this: she was sitting on a box of dead people (grey tin box) "Open the lid"; in a ruined building with water running down the walls (mother is a ruin, frightening, dark, dank walls) "This is you"; she was with someone, (she quite liked it) "What's she doing sitting on my box?", who said, "Let's open it." In the box were four bodies face down (I wanted to sit on the lid to suffocate them, they were not quite dead) "I'm beautiful", "I'm warm and secure", "I'm dead", "I'll leave her"; the last one, a man in a brown suit (dull, nondescript, husband?) walked away carrying with him a small deed box "I'm taking the soul with me." We improvised a Splitting of the people sitting on the box – the Suffocators – and the people being suffocated. As Suffocator she felt just heavy and dull with slow thudding drum beats. Being suffocated, she played with the liveliest drum and cymbal clashes I had heard from her, feeling vehemently, "I *won't* be suffocated!" There were memories, when we talked afterwards, of being shut in her room at two, a feeling that through her phobia her creative side was being suffocated and the keen realisation of both the energy and will for life in this part of her as well as the fear of exposure and challenge of growth. Some time later she told me of a secret suitcase full of stories which she had written which no one except her husband had ever seen.

DREAM RESOLUTION

In this exercise the client goes back and finds, in an improvisation, another ending to the kind of unsatisfactory or frightening dream from which one wakes in a state of disturbance or haunted feeling which can last for days, weeks or even years. It is a most reassuring experience, rather like tidying a room internally. The only recorded example which I have is unfortunately quite unfit for this kind of publication.

SHELLS, STONES, SAND AND SOUNDS

This technique can have an almost hypnotically calming effect or, occasionally, one of extreme irritation. It is based on the experience of sitting on the seashore idly arranging shells to the sound of the sea. The client sits by the chime bars with a tray of white sand and a bowl of shells and stones, and while the therapist answers her on the xylophone and cymbal (with wire brush only) she places a shell (or stone) on to the sand. She then repeats this process until she has had enough. She is not told to have any conscious focus, just to do it. But this idle meaninglessness can bring out the deepest meaning. Very often a client who is blocking expression in one modality cannot resist allowing herself an outlet through another.

Example 1
A woman in her forties, experiencing "emptiness", started by playing small steps up and down the scale getting stronger and stronger. As I played angrily on the cymbal, responding to counter-transference, she sought deeper tones and played first "Killing" the notes (stopping the vibration with the beater) and then letting them sing. She took a long time over it. With shells she made two neat families, of six at the bottom right hand corner and five further up. Afterwards she talked about her love "killing people off". There were six in her parents' family, then the father died leaving five.

Example 2
Another woman, a busy professional with a family, made a harmonious design filling the whole tray and played measured tones. She felt it was a marvellous "held" feeling, like being a child who is helped but not interfered with by an adult in conversation. A satisfying non-verbal experience like this does not always call for explanation and investigation; it can be its own good reason for being.

16. Yet more techniques of analytical music therapy

Most of the techniques described in this chapter are designed to keep the ego much more firmly in control of matters than those in the last chapter. The first three techniques are suitable for later treatment when the loosening up of the access of the unconscious has done its work and there is a greater need for tightening up and achieving conscious control and creativity in external reality.

REALITY REHEARSAL

When the client has reached a point of decision as to a direction to be taken in external life, she is ready for a reality rehearsal. The purpose of this technique is to raise, face, and eventually overcome or come to terms with all those inner fears, anxieties, ambivalences and negative and destructive urges which wait beside the pathway to the desired aim. Having been thus faced and at least partially overcome, they are not likely to surprise and overwhelm her when she really sets out for the interview, to the altar, to the examination or whatever the situation is, nor will they be so likely to wait for her in the small hours alone later on. Certain occult schools talk about this psychological reality as the "Dweller on the threshold" who must be reckoned with before certain pathways can be entered. The saying, "No one who puts his hand to the plough and looks back is fit for the kingdom of God", could also suggest the idea of progress being impeded by something having been left behind and not dealt with at the outset.

In this technique the client imagines that she is taking her new step and while keeping all her expression for her sense of purpose and endeavour, she allows herself to experience inwardly any fears and negative urges which may arise, afterwards sharing these verbally with the therapist and possibly examining them musically too. It is a well known phenomenon that at the end of treatment or psychoanalysis there can be a return of symptoms as a kind of Dweller at the Gateway of the new independent life. This technique goes to meet this phenomenon in a creative, constructive way just as the youth in the fairy story took food to appease the watch-dogs.

Example 1

A young wife of 26, with young children in a floundering marriage. Her husband came to ask for a reconciliation and she wanted to improvise "Making a go of it". Her playing was spasmodic, finally fading out, but she had a pleasant fantasy of painting the children's room and making love.

It is interesting to note that so many clients who can express intense emotion on the negative side (this client was remarkable for it) find it extremely difficult to invest emotion in a positive aim. This is something that has to be learnt. They imagine that the ideal will produce the emotion, as in the negative expression, whereas they must evoke and inject the expression into the idea and will its continuation. In the first case they are tapping a repressed but available source of energy and in the second they are acting as an energy producer and director, which is much more difficult.

WHOLENESS

After all the techniques of Splitting, Holding and dipping into the great sea of the unconscious, this technique comes as quite a shock. The client plays alone, on any instruments she chooses, while the therapist listens. She is told to play as if she were perfectly whole.

Example 1

A woman of 40 said: "I sat in silence for a long while, feeling my power, almost like a god before creation. I felt my lack of balance, my dependence on some people and my vital negative resistance to others. Where was my balance? My wholeness? I felt that I had never had such total permission-to-be before and I was terrified. The therapist's calm presence held me to my endeavour. Finally I struck the gong. The responsibility was total. I played some more but all the time I felt that I was creased up in my non-wholeness of reaction and rebellion like a snail suddenly deprived of its inner-wrinkled shell. What had I gained? The potent moment of questioning. I often return to that moment in the bustle of life. It has given me a kind of secret point of growth."

EXPLORING RELATIONSHIPS

This can be done in a variety of ways: the client being the other party and letting the therapist be her as in the Splitting technique; just playing, with the partner's name as title as in Emotional Investment; or acting out different kinds of relationship musically. The emotional expression in the music seems to enable the client to receive valuable insights without the need to be told anything by the therapist. Indeed spoken words might be given at a level of understanding at which she might find the insights unassimilable.

Example 1

A man of 35 reported that his marriage was not going well but did not immediately tell that he had been having brief extramarital affairs. The therapist and client tried different ways of relating in music. First the client went his way and the therapist, as wife, went hers. Then each listened to the other while playing. Next he followed her and lastly she followed him. Afterwards he said that he liked the second way of relationship best and went on to talk very freely about his life and loves. At last he came round to feeling that the main thing that he was aware of was his great need of his wife. This session had no follow-up as the client was discharged.

Example 2

A married woman, 28, with children, explored her feelings about her lover. Improvising on his name she played with an unusually steady and guarded beat saying afterwards that she had felt love, sexual feelings and happiness but had got through to the feeling that she did not really want to leave her husband and children. The affair subsequently broke up.

Example 3

A man of 32 with angry feelings at the mother who had left him when he was four was told to tell me (as Mother) in sound all the angry feelings that he had about my going and I was to state the mother's feelings back in sound. He pounded and drummed and clashed the cymbals with enormous fierceness and then the whole feeling flowed so beautifully into words beginning, "I feel angry and bitter . . ." and carrying on a whole argument without stopping for seven minutes.

AFFIRMATIONS

Music therapy is not all storm and stress. There are moments of joy and peace in life which even in memory have a revivifying effect on the body through the imagination. Sometimes a client can experience a resurgence of hope and faith through getting in touch with these experiences.

Example 1
A married woman, 26, took the title "The Happiest Moment in My Life" and went back three years to the time when her baby was born. Although referred to the therapist by the psychiatrist as "lacking in confidence" she had the courage to choose to play the piano for this improvisation leaving the therapist the other instruments, and she played really beautiful music. Afterwards, describing the experience, the therapist said that her eyes shone with happiness and she looked quite radiant. The depression was momentarily banished.

SUB-VERBAL COMMUNICATION
This technique consists of the therapeutic couple just playing without titles or focus but sometimes with a time limit of – say – five, ten or twenty minutes. It can be a very powerful experience, even a trainee music therapist who had been through analysis said, "One is not prepared for what may come up." I use this technique when embarrassment is blocking the client's real feelings through words, when I feel that there is some difficulty in expression arising from negative or positive transference feelings or when I feel that the client is thoroughly dried out with words.

Example 1
The client was a student unable to find her centre. We played for ten minutes – perhaps we did have an unspoken title: "From the Centre" – her mechanical playing became more and more secure and then louder and then very sensitive and real as we ended. The client became aware of these changes towards a more inner-directed (centrifugal) playing.

Example 2
A married woman of 35, with children, was splitting her transference between me, as good therapist, and a former therapist, as bad. With no title or focus we played for ten minutes. She gradually expressed more and more fierce feelings on the cymbal and drum which I answered, and then at the end she expressed great tenderness. This gave us some really fierce and tender feelings within the session to talk about and it was followed by more fury in some correspondence to me later on, of which we were able to make good use in a

subsequent session. She began to tolerate ambivalent feelings towards one person.

PATTERNS OF SIGNIFICANCE

This technique is used to discover the inner pattern and feelings surrounding significant events in life. It is particularly useful for clients in the second half of life. The main events used as titles so far have been Death, Birth, Giving Birth and Marriage. The improvisation on "Death" can cover physical death, losing a job or a limb, experiencing loss of any kind. "Birth" can be one's physical birth, birth into the adult world, any kind of initiation of entry into a new job or phase of life. "Giving Birth" may be an ordinary labour, the birth of a work of art or idea, and "Marriage" can be two people uniting as man and wife, two people in any complementary working relationship or the creative and receptive Yin-Yang powers coming together in fertile embrace in the developing psyche.

The results of this technique are in the form of feelings and yet they can have the strangely moving quality of a reality more persuasive than all the outer events of Monday to Sunday. The therapist plays as in the Holding technique.

Example 1

An unmarried woman of 50 improvised "Marriage". There was before her a valley like a rocky, bronze chalice in which there were stony hollows echoing one to the other, and she thought of the words, "Deep calling unto deep". There was a feeling of great width and no sense of nearness, closeness or anything personal. By countertransference the therapist had the intuition to play these deep sounds. When they finished the therapist suggested that the great bowl could be her late mother's marriage and all her relationships might have been held within this. The client was told to go back and break up the valley. She felt very apprehensive about this when she started but she went at it with a will and as the drum boomed and cymbals clashed, gods and goddesses were hurled among the rocks as the valley broke up. Next there were dark green shoots of grass and a patch of pure white sand (possibly male and female symbols). She felt rather uneasy at this and then felt that she was stuck. As we played on she saw a trickle of water get bigger and bigger until it became a fountain in whose bubbling waters she bathed with a feeling of deep satisfaction. There was much to discuss and think about from this improvisation.

Example 2
A teacher of 32 played an improvisation "Giving Birth". His playing
was very delicate at the beginning when he had the feeling of something growing bigger and bigger inside him. With heavy drum beats
he felt that it had to come out but that it was difficult to detach
himself from it. The final music expressed his terrible sadness
because he felt that he had lost something. He said, "It was all very
selfish, I tried to think it was succeeding and being happy in its
success but there was this undercurrent of deep sadness." We were
then able to discuss how this resembled his feelings about letting
his able pupils go out into the world when their studies were finished.

SUICIDE
This technique is used to allow clients – or more often patients – who
want to kill themselves, to go through the feelings about such an
experience. However, they are also asked, whatever they believe, to
imagine for the sake of the exercise, that they have not gone out
like a light but remain conscious, though invisible, and go and
revisit their family and friends without, however, being able to speak
to them or touch them. It is not a technique that is used lightly and
never (outside the Intertherap) unless the patient seriously brings
up her wish for death by her own hand.

Example 1
This is an example of the use of this technique in an emergency
together with other techniques. A wife, the mother of an 18-month-
old child, suffering from moodswing, came to the psychodynamic
movement session saying that she felt so awful that she wanted to
die. It happened that she was the only patient to come to the session
that day. Her face was pale and puffy and her eyes somehow veiled.
We put on Indian music saying that we would all dance the feeling
of wanting to withdraw. Suddenly there was a splintering crash;
she had pushed the glass out of one of the windows and stood still,
stunned. I examined her hands. Owing to the gauze curtains in
front of the windows they were quite unscathed. She wanted to lie
down so I gave her a cushion and rug and kept up two-way communication. Mr O. came in, having swept away the glass outside and
said perhaps she would really let us feel her anger and pain in sound.
She agreeed and while Mr O. played on the piano she raged on the
drum and cymbal, her face contorted with rage and dark hair flying.
When she had finished she said would she have to be locked up now.

"If you think so, go and tell the Sister. You are grown up," I said. She replied that she didn't feel it. Mr O. asked her to play being the age she felt. "About three," she said starting to play in a very stilted way and getting gradually wilder and wilder and crashing on the cymbal. I asked her about her brothers and sisters. She had one brother, he was 18 months old when she was three, the same age as her own child whom she dared not look after. It looked like a displacement of her early jealousy. She then improvised on a suicide by being run over by a train. It was very wild and she stopped when she was dead saying "I feel fine." That is the moment the therapist dreads so we quickly asked her to go back and visit her family. She played for some time and stopped on the point of tears saying that she loved them so but was no good to them now. Her distress was very real. She then talked perfectly coherently for some time with shining eyes, high colour and her face looking somehow thinner. Without any extra sedation she spent the rest of the day in helping sensibly with the chores. Of course she was not cured of her very severe disorder by this but she was much alleviated and it helped her to communicate in a more normal manner.

Example 2

A wife and mother in her thirties, with compulsive urges to snatch up broken glass and knives and try to cut her wrists in order to kill herself, improvised her suicide completely through. She experienced killing herself, being happy thinking, "I've done it", then finding that she was unable to communicate with her family; going to her dead relatives and discovering that "I could not talk to them because my distress at what I had done put them out of my reach", and then coming back to her family and being distraught at not being able to be seen by them. This patient also had a very serious disturbance and she was certainly not cured by this exercise but she did come to realise how much her children meant to her and their photo, which she would hold in her hands, helped her to withstand these impulses many times.

PROGRAMMED REGRESSION

During periods of emotional disturbance people very often regress and live partly as if they were at an earlier age, as did the young mother in the Suicide Example 1. By making the regression conscious it is easier for them to be aware of what is happening and also to return to the present. Clients are not asked to "try to remember being six" (or whatever the desired age is), they are simply told to be that age and start playing. This has never seemed to present them with the slightest difficulty. The emotions released are usually strong and frequently accompanied by vivid memory pictures of outer and inner events of that time. In the case of very early regression one cannot check up on the memory of the pre-verbal images but they seem to be of significance to the patients who produce them. Whether they really are images from their earliest infancy or feelings about that time one cannot know, but in going through such regression improvisation one can experience such a power of emotion, feel the being of the prescribed age so vividly, that I see no reason to imagine that there is a certain tender age earlier than which all this ceases and there is no more possible memory. This technique is useful for tapping the reservoir of the unexpressed in the past or for finding out at what age a certain fear or feeling began. The therapist uses the Holding technique or sometimes uses a Splitting technique with significant characters from the scenes remembered.

Example 1

A young married woman with children told the story of how she had found her sister in bed with her husband. When I asked what her reaction had been, she said that she had said, "Charming!", and walked out. I suggested that she relive the scene but express her real feelings about the situation with me. She drummed furiously for several minutes with wild shrieks of "Fucking bitch!".

It was not a matter of working herself up to it, the emotion came right out at once in this otherwise rather precise and controlled young woman.

Example 2

Joan, a phobic woman of 36, brought up the feeling of being let down on her birthday. We improvised on her second birthday, she used the drum and said it was "a happy little party"; the third birthday, using the drum and cymbal was happy. On her fourth birthday, playing on the xylophone, she felt rather lost. It was just pre-war. Then she said that she couldn't remember her fifth birthday. I replied that she was not asked to remember but just be there and play. It was deep, sad music. When Joan finished she remembered that the nursery helper who had shown her all her dresses, including the one that she would have worn for the party, had been suddenly dismissed by Joan's father and Joan had felt so embarrassed. It was interesting how the music, in expressing her emotions, unblocked her memory of this baffling childhood event.

Example 3

A young wife, anxious about separation from anyone for whom she cared deeply, went back to the age of 12 when her uncle had taken her to visit her much loved dying aunt in a cancer ward. The music was quite stormy and violent with hints of panic. She had not been able to tell anyone her feelings at the time. "I just wanted to get out," she said. This battle of love and fear had been locked up in her for years.

Example 4

A widow with moodswing, 60 years old, went back to five minutes old. She was aware of light and bright colour, but around her and coming towards her was a shadow. This she managed to condense into the symbol of a cloaked figure – she said it was the figure of Death. In a later session she had images of Light and Darkness and their interaction. Light wanted Darkness to go away by becoming engulfed by it. Darkness wanted to accompany Light wherever it went and said it was there first. (It is interesting to note that another victim of moodswing, working with a different analytical music therapist, had had a similar figure of incredible darkness and evil which she became aware of in her "Birth" improvisation.)

17. The emotional spectrum

During my music therapy training period, it became apparent that as the work of a music therapist was to be essentially with the emotions, it was necessary for me to find some convenient way of mapping out this area of function. I thought about it deeply and finally devised the conceptual model of the emotional spectrum. The target-shaped design was taken from Dr Alexander Lowen's diagram of Hate surrounding a central core of Love.* The placing of the seven main emotions was based on the study of the pathway taken by some of the autistic children described by Dr Bruno Bettelheim in making their way back to normal function, and also the way people have broken down, or broken through, at marathon group therapy sessions.

There are, of course, many more words for emotions than those given on the spectrum, but those are compound emotions. Jealousy, for instance, is a compound of love, fear and anger. Respect is a blend of love and freeze-fear. Pride can be love of self with defensive fear. Depression can be a mixture of sorrow, guilt and freeze-fear covering up anger.

In this model each emotion has its positive and negative aspect. The three central emotions of love, joy and peace form a triad which should be fairly evenly balanced. In some people love is the tonic, joy the dominant and peace the mediant. In others the tonic is joy or peace. Most people are under-expressing in one of them and need to work consciously at restoring the balance. This can be done usefully through music therapy.

The various emotions given are no more exact than at what point between 600 Mu and 500 Mu yellow turns to green. Nevertheless they can be a useful rough guide in the therapist's work. Here is an explanation of the spectrum.

FREEZE-FEAR. +7
In animal life this is the first response of the rabbit to danger. It
* The diagram is on p. 151.

serves a useful purpose in humans when it enables them to think and understand what it would be best to do rather than plunging ahead recklessly.

−7. In its negative aspect freeze-fear can be seen in psychiatric illness as catatonia. As body tension it can take a less drastic form as a protection against desired but feared acts of violence or sexual appetite. It can also be the cause of an inability to decide, act, feel or think.

FLIGHT-FEAR. +6

In fleeing from what is harmful this is a normal, healthy response.

−6. In its negative aspect it can be heedless panic flight or flight into physical or psychiatric illness.

DEFENSIVE FEAR. +5

Any normal, useful defence of one's person, property or values comes into this category.

−5. This is the sort of behaviour which is unadaptably defensive all the time. −5 oriented characters act like alarmed hedgehogs and rhinos and are difficult to communicate with unless one remembers the vulnerability inside and addresses oneself to this. Protective compulsive ritualistic and obsessive behaviour come into this category.

ANGER. +4

This is righteous indignation and willingness to take aggression on behalf of the self or its objects and values.

When it turns into violent destruction it is −4.

GUILT. +3

This is a useful emotion when its pain produces change for the better but it is too often combined with the negative aspect of freeze-fear and frozen solid.

−3 is the urge to destroy the self, either quickly and dramatically or slowly through abuse of alcohol or drugs. It very often follows negative, or even positive, feelings of anger. It could be argued that it is a kind of negative anger. But it is not, as the aggression is directed inward, it has quite another quality although it can be identification with an outer persecutor who is supposed to be feeling negative anger.

SORROW. +2
This is a tremendously healing emotion where it is allowed to flow freely, which usually it is not. About unexpressed grief Dr E. P. Gramlich* writes, "Physical symptomatology is a common part of grief and chronic grief may be manifested by chronic physical symptoms either due to diagnosable psychosomatic conditions or ill-defined symptoms of pain and dysfunction. Parkes lists osteoarthritis, colitis, spastic colon, urticaria, migraine, asthma, bronchitis, ulcerative colitis as disease entities which may be precipitated or aggravated by a loss."

−2, self-pity is one of the most invidious and poisoning emotions which prevents further development by its passive masochistic orientation.

LOVE. +1a
This is a warm giving and receiving.

−1a. Desire is the awareness of a need, a kind of dynamic emptiness.

JOY. +1b
This is a vitalising force expressive of delight.

−1b. Mania is used in this context as any hollow joy based on a defence against or blocking out of other emotions and is seen at its worst in the manic stage of affective disorders.

PEACE. +1c
This brings serenity to the character.

−1c is apathy. Not the tense inactivity of negative freeze-fear but a self-satisfied, sluggish state of being.

RECORDING THE EMOTIONS IN CASE NOTES
The numerals on the spectrum make it a suitable way of recording the emotions expressed through different parts of the body. Imagine, for example, treating an aphasic child. His only communication will be non-verbal sounds or body expression. When making the case notes these can be neatly recorded. Draw a rough sketch of the child – a pin man will do – and then record numerically the emotions that showed themselves in the session on the appropriate parts of the body. For example little John, an undersized autistic boy of 11, only showed a −4 aggressive response in his clacking teeth for many weeks. This would be normal for a feeding baby. His hands,

* See bibliography, p. 267.

at this time, only showed −7 freeze-fear reaction, being clutched inwards on his chest. One week he came in when I was drinking my morning coffee. With a rush he threw himself on me and grabbed for the coffee. I was able to record his −1 and −4 response in the hands that evening. Notably enough, the −4 did not return to the teeth during that session.

In an interview a client may be responsive and smiling but expressing −7 with her legs and hands, and the freeze-fear may be a cover for her −4 in the hands and a habitual −1a response in the legs. The possibility of recording these emotional responses in the body makes the therapist more alert to their appearance and change, and able to plot the dynamic flow of emotional expression through the body over a period of time.

THE EMOTIONAL SPECTRUM AS ASSESSMENT TOOL

The emotional spectrum has proved to be a useful assessment tool at a client's first interview. The therapist presents the client with the basic emotion titles written on cards and places these on the floor. It is unnecessary at this stage to explain about the negative aspects, the client may interpret them as she will. Sitting before a battery of instruments, the client – who is usually in an acute state of −7 – finds it relatively easy to express this in sound. Her playing is taped and played back to her when she will usually respond with a great deal of useful information about her thoughts concerning this emotion, also special occasions in her life when she experienced it as destructive or helpful. From there the therapist proceeds through the whole spectrum.

It is important to observe how much of her body the client involves in playing the different emotions. For example, a young psychiatrist expressing the fears used nothing but his wrists and hands. He warmed up towards the centre of the spectrum involving his shoulders in anger and his whole back and abdomen and legs in love. In his job he was habitually used to inhibiting negative fear responses but was successful in his work and a happily married man who found full expression in loving.

Here are examples of brief notes from emotional spectrum tests on a postgraduate student and a businessman.

Emotion	Student	Businessman
FREEZE-FEAR	Played from above, tapped, high	Couldn't do it

FLIGHT-FEAR	Fierce thuddy, gentle withdrawal on cymbal	Glissando on xylophone
DEFENSIVE FEAR	Very fierce	Very violent
ANGER	Rather organised and jolly	Tremendous outburst
GUILT	Cymbal insidious, connected to depression	Couldn't do it
SORROW	Gentle, beautiful xylophone	Thoughtful
LOVE	Strong, 4/4 on cymbal	Couldn't do it
JOY	4/4 happy, alive	Conventional rhythm
PEACE	Crescendo on cymbal	Sensitive

What did it mean? The answer cannot be given exactly in words. These are clues to which the therapist responds intuitively. But a little more information may be helpful. The student had a tendency for flight into illness. Her positive use of aggression was not free and was subsequently successfully developed through music therapy and used to her greater advantage. Too much of her personality was built round defending against being told how to be, instead of getting on with it and actually being herself. Love had been a positive experience. Guilt was negative but only very mildly.

The businessman was using his aggression to the full; he was very defended, even to the point of refusing to attempt to express emotions which he found troublesome. His flight-fear in life expressed itself in a constant whirl of activity. His playing of sorrow and peace showed that he was in touch with the more sensitive part of his psyche. After quite a number of sessions he was expressing love musically with gusto and agreeable lack of inhibition, and could accept freeze-fear and guilt as having their part in the scheme of things.

EXPERIENCE IN GROUPS WITH THE EMOTIONAL SPECTRUM

I have had interesting experiences going through the emotional spectrum with groups of psychiatric patients, each in turn playing their sound expression of the same emotion. Anger always brought out very lively emotional discharge in the listeners through laughter. They were well able to express the fears. Flight-fear provoked some amusement. Defensive fear produced a high casualty rate among instruments. Guilt produced seriousness on the whole with some sniggers and guffaws by an element which was troubled by feelings about masturbation. Most people found guilt hard to express but all talked about it interestingly afterwards. Sorrow brought on an atmosphere of intense interest and electric expectation; it seemed to be a depth of experience that all had plumbed but never spoken about freely before. There was tense silence and rapt attention during performances. Love was found to be very difficult to express in

positive

Map of emotional territory

Source: A. Lowen, *Love and Orgasm*

sound but for this reason the verbal communication following performances was most enlightening. It is the effort which is most helpful, the result is less important.

After two terms of sound expression in this manner, I found that the same patients were quite expressive and fluent in making small impromptu speeches to the group describing incidents using these emotions. When we began it was difficult to provoke more than a monosyllable or short sentence in response to a question.

OTHER USES OF THE EMOTIONAL SPECTRUM

It can be useful for the music therapy student to practise studying emotional patterns by recording the emotions of a character in any novel which she is reading, then comparing the character's pattern with her own. A church group co-operated in making an emotional spectrum plotting of the recorded expressions of the emotions of Jesus in one gospel. It was interesting to see how many +4 notations there were in spite of the popular "meek and mild" image.

18. The joint session

WHO NEEDS IT?

The joint session can be useful for helping any two people who interact frequently: married couples, members of long-term heterosexual or homosexual relationships, working partners whose interpersonal understanding is essential for the right atmosphere around their job, parent/child relationships and so on, people who want to find out what lies behind their disturbing emotional reactions to and attacks upon one another.

The couple may come to therapy as a dyadic unit with an equal wish on both sides to investigate their problems (which gives the best possible condition for work) or one may drag the other along, in which case the therapist will probably start off by helping them to explore the feelings of the reluctant partner. A third possibility is that a client who is having analytical music therapy develops and grows so that her partner outside therapy becomes out of tune with her new level of functioning. Perhaps a husband originally sent his sick wife along hoping that she would be sent back "just like she used to be", as if she were some kind of machine needing a spare-part replacement and a quick oiling of all other moving parts. Instead she may work on herself with her therapy, develop, and with luck overcome the need for the original complaint and quite outgrow the person she once was. This may prove uncomfortable for the husband. It is as if he took a xylophone in for repair and was given back a grand piano. This great instrument has to be played skilfully with the fingers. Where is his nice little instrument that he could hit with beaters? Gone forever. But through a period of joint sessions the couple can begin to explore their new relationship, with the therapist containing the aspirations and feelings of the complete dyad and holding the ability of each one of them to think and feel under this interpersonal stress without the partnership breaking up. In this way these tensions can begin to be worked out in the session rather than avoided or attacked one-sidedly at home and then acted out as adultery, cruelty or desertion by the other partner.

WHAT IS THE AIM OF A JOINT SESSION?

The aim of a joint session is to preserve a partnership while the feelings about it are being explored and expressed, in such a way that growth and development can take place and another, more creative, relationship interaction may emerge. The interaction between the partners is what the trio are investigating, but this is based on individual feelings which again come from resonances from the past. Could this not be done by each partner individually in therapy? There are certain aspects of the work which cannot be replaced in individual therapy. One is the partners' interaction here and now in the presence of the therapist. Another is the very affecting sight of one partner struggling to work on herself and laying bare all her aggression, fears and weaknesses honestly, whereas she had formerly been dealing with them by projecting them all on to the other partner. The memory of this is a powerful aid to self-control, support and tolerance in the daily life which follows the session. A third factor is the experience of the actual music played together. The possibility of the tolerance and even creative use of one another's fierce emotions, the sensitive responses to the sad and gentle sounds and the delight in the resilient interaction of the playful interludes. These are not "just music" but real relationship possibilities in embryo, seminal experiences. Not being words they cannot be contradicted or rationalised away. They remain.

MANAGEMENT

To study the session on tape, it is easiest if each partner has the same kinds of instrument but of a distinguishable pitch, so that the therapist can hear who played which sforzando crash or gentle response. I suggest that ideally each partner should have a protesting instrument – a drum – and an annihilating instrument – one a cymbal, the other a gong – and a simple pitch instrument – perhaps one a xylophone and the other a kalimba or melodica, plus any desired pleasant-sounding instruments such as flat-clappered hand-bells, fine-toned Indian cymbals, maracas and suchlike.

The partners can sit side by side with the therapist facing them when he sits in the chair, the piano being wherever is convenient. This gives the feeling that each one is going to work on him or herself and they are not inextricably linked but that their interaction is by conscious choice. If, however, there is the need to have a greater feeling of intimacy such as in an unconsummated marriage, then the couple can sit face to face and use a certain amount of eye contact during their music.

Why should the analytical music therapist play with them? The therapist will help the partners with the music of the unconscious unexpressed part of the relationship, being a channel for the dyadic counter-transference. If they have a taboo on tenderness, he will be playing the tenderness. If it is a "never had a cross word" partnership, he will have it for them. But he will not play all the time. Sometimes they will have a duet and he will listen, but they are seldom ready to do this at once. First they must be introduced to the full range of the emotional spectrum through the trio playing together.

If the partners are both attending for the first time it is advisable to start by asking them for a brief history of the relationship, other relationships, family backgrounds, with accent on the relationship between each one and their siblings and parents. The interaction, dominance or submissiveness, corrections and roles will be noted by the therapist as part of their relationship pattern. Then the music can begin and after this the feelings behind the facts will start to flow. If they start with the expression of feelings it may be impossible to elicit any further factual information at all at that session and the therapist will have lost the valuable anonymity factor by the next session.

TECHNIQUES

For a resilient couple a useful improvisation to begin with is an expression of all that they feel is wrong with the other. In this way each will withdraw a certain amount of the energy used in projecting these feelings into their partners, and in consequence will feel that much less in need of defending themselves against these feelings in the other.

With joint sessions the Splitting improvisation often has to be done with a reversal of roles to get to grips with a dyadic phenomenon which I term Emotional Portering. As an example: Mr G. came to analytical music therapy saying that his wife was terrified of what the treatment might do to him. Closer investigation through a joint interview revealed that she was nothing of the kind; he was giving her these fears to carry, which meant that he, as passenger, had only the noblest sentiments of 'worry about my wife' to offer me. He was asked to play as his Wife With The Fears. Had this been a joint session she could have played her husband being worried about her and the situation could have been opened up.

Verbal communication blocks can form when both partners are sending out emotive dialogue at the same time. Not so in music. But the emotional pattern underlying the dialogue can be usefully taken apart and explored musically. For example: Mrs V. could not stand her husband's broody silences. When Mr V. played the music of his feelings behind these silences they were terrifying fortissimo drumming assaults. Mrs V. was asked how it felt just to take that. "Like being murdered," she said. Mr V. admitted that he had felt like murdering – not Mrs V. – but an inner image of a great writhing serpent with his mother's head on it. Already this bit of information made this behaviour a little bit more tolerable to Mrs V. She did not feel so responsible or so threatened.

A useful technique with married couples is to ask each in turn to lead (as in a concerto) an improvisation on their ideal view of their partner's role (The Ideal Wife/Husband), then talk, then improvise on the role as played by their spouse (My Wife/Husband) and discuss the feelings about the difference. The therapist must ask himself, "What are these two people doing to each other?" in music and what are they doing in words, then see how these two forms of behaviour differ or relate. Usually the musical communication will complement the verbal but the emotion will first emerge in the music.

Unending frustration in a relationship comes from one partner trying to amend the situation through the other. Clients come to realise that in music therapy they cannot be sure of anything but their own feelings; they cannot work with anything but their own feelings; they cannot change a situation except from within themselves. This is the only reliable control they have. It is sometimes argued that this is being selfish. But a person who knows how she feels and what changes she is prepared to make, can be negotiated with, while a person whose only knowledge is about the misdemeanours and unlovely attributes of her partner has not even got a starting place. The therapist can endeavour to help each partner to find such a secure centre and to find the centre of the dyad as a whole.

Composite emotions can be usefully taken apart and improvisations done on each component. Jealousy is a common problem in a joint session. With Mr and Mrs L. her hate of the object of her jealousy was played first, with Mr L. just Holding in the background with me. She was not asked to speak about this but told to play Fear, which was very wild and sad. Again she was asked to play at once, this time Love which was very central and firm. This was followed by quite a torrent of words about all she valued in

Mr L. who was visibly touched as at home her words had never got further than the Hate aspect of this composite emotion. Later on she spoke more calmly of the other two aspects but now there was the realisation of what she was defending. A fruitful discussion ensued.

The rage behind impotence or frigidity can come out very clearly in music when one partner is the victim of the other's paradoxical communication. Mrs L. said that she felt that her husband was "pushing and pulling" her, encouraging her verbally to be sexually active and then repelling her loving physical advances. She played the feeling of being invited "all warmth and joy", and then the cold, abrupt repulsion "cutting something off inside me". But when she improvised the feeling of the two together she drummed in a veritable frenzy of rage. Mr L. was quite disturbed at the realisation of how his behaviour affected his wife when he heard it in decibels. It was enough to start him exploring very seriously why he did this.

NOTES ON TWO JOINT SESSIONS

Mrs E., 30, an overprotected middle daughter of three, was a housewife (with twin children) who had been in hospital with depression and suicidal attempts which usually followed quarrels with her husband. Mr E., 34, was a skilled worker, he came from a large family and when his wife was ill he patiently took over the mothering role in the home, cooking, washing, cleaning and minding the children when he came home from work. Following her analytical music therapy Mrs E., formerly frigid, gained interest in sex through extramarital experiments and said that she would like to get divorced. At this point joint sessions were suggested, by the consultant psychotherapist who had referred her for music therapy, in order to explore the marriage relationship. The couple agreed.

Session 1

Mr and Mrs E. arrived late. I explained that I was only there to help them to investigate their feelings about their marriage. All decisions and valuations were their own. I started by saying that we would be looking at what was wrong but would start by playing a "Validation of the other", thinking of the good qualities of the partner. (Though this was psychologically reassuring it was not a very good idea musically speaking, I decided later, not being inducive to tension release.)

Music: Mr E. started with a sulky drum ostinato, Mrs E. played

157

big steps up and down the xylophone then interacted with me, there came more excitement into the music, I had an interaction with Mr E. and Mrs E. angrily rang the bells. At the end Mr E. slightly altered his beat.

Words: Mr E. said that he loved Mrs E. and had thought her a good mother and good but "compulsive" housewife. Did she realise this? No, but even if she had what happened would still have happened, she said. Mr E. felt that he had three children. She felt that he was a parent. She was sorry for what she had done and felt that he must be ashamed of her. (Her jealousy of her husband entering her session came out clearly only in the music.)

The next improvisation was "Marriage".

Music: Quite fierce and determined rhythm, Mrs E., on tambourine and timid bells, exploring on xylophone, Mr E.'s drum ostinato ending with little protests at Mrs E.'s drumming.

Words: Mrs E. said that it was so boring, children and housework, same routine every day. Mr E. said that his work was routine and boring, too, but that he did get out every day. He said that he was old-fashioned and thought that once you were married that was it, and he wondered what effect their marriage was having on the children. Mrs E. said that he was right really and mentioned something said by their daughter. I pointed out that they both seemed to be saying that excitement was something that one got from outside the marriage. Mr E. said that Mrs E. only liked 'compulsive' shopping and going out. I wondered if Mrs E. was not cheating herself by not using her creativity in the rest of the day. Mr E. said that if she wanted to try and go it alone he would stick around as she was sure to fail. Should a husband be a safety net? we wondered.

The next improvisation was "Listening to each other", a duet.

Music: Gentle, Mr E. ostinato, Mrs E.'s playing sounded like knocking to get in, they were together at the end. (I had to stop them as time was getting short and they showed no sign of stopping.)

For "Not listening":

Music: Very lively, banging crotchets from Mr E., angry bells from Mrs E., accelerando together and at the end Mr E. drumming like fury. (I had also to stop this.) There was no time for talking but it evidently gave them permission to continue a verbal edition of this musical dialogue at home.

Session 2

A week later. Mr E. had abandoned his safety-net attitude and told

158

Mrs E. that if she could not remain faithful he would divorce her. To give an idea of the greater possible scope of a marriage, I had made eight cards on which were written Dr H. V. Dicks' eight "fairly natural functions" of marital life: sexual, affection and personal respect, child-rearing, domestic "chores", financial and family policy, social (friends, in-laws), cultural and leisure, and religion and political values. We started by expressing our negative feelings in an improvisation called "Spring cleaning":

Music: Fierce banging, piano worked up a terrific crescendo, Mrs E. banging on the drum, Mr E. ostinato, Mrs E. on drum too but with irregular beating, Mr E. burst out on the cymbal for the first time and then identified with the piano's music.

Words: Not recorded.

Mrs E. chose "Affection and personal respect":

Music: Mr E. mezzo piano on cymbal, lyrical piano, Mrs E. gentle xylophone and bells.

Words: Mrs E. said that she found it hard to be affectionate and say "Thank you" for her husband's gifts, she felt that he thought that she did not respect him. Mr E. said that he respected her in front of friends, children and relatives, thought her adultery showed no respect to him; he gave presents to her and sweets to the twins as affection.

Mr E. chose "Social (friends and in-laws)":

Music: Mr E. begins, jogging along, Mrs E. goes up and down on xylophone, piano anonymous then playful, glissando down, Mr E. answers on the cymbal, Mrs E. gives a tambourine crescendo then interacts with the piano on the maracas, Mrs E. plays gentle bells and Mr E. plays mezzo piano on the cymbal.

Words: Mr E. started talking all about his wife's social life. I gently asked him about his own. He had work friends, otherwise only friends shared by Mrs E. His family were so large that they were not really interested in them, they saw his parents seldom. Mrs E. wanted more friends and thought that was why she had had boy-friends and sex; they went out together and there seemed to be nothing else to do when the conversation ran out and the pubs closed.

I chose "Domestic chores".

Music: Typical of their home life this was one long solo by Mr E. on cymbal, pianissimo, then drum, then cymbal.

Words: Mrs E. said that she hadn't heard me or understood. She was dominated by chores but Mr E. wasn't. He was quite practical and methodical about them but not "compulsive", he said.

This was one of the cases where the spouse invited in feels increasingly threatened by the situation at first. Mr E. felt that he was well and Mrs E. was ill. Everything would be all right if she were different. On top of this Mrs E., who had been my patient for five months, was jealous of him coming in. For several sessions Mrs E. came alone, Mr E. had "forgotten" or "wasn't bothered", she said. Then a further joint session with the consultant psychotherapist opened up Mr E.'s anxiety and persuaded him of the value of his continued attendance. They resumed joint sessions with me. After the second, following a very gloomy improvisation on "Sundays", Mrs E. took another overdose in the night and once again came into hospital. The husband and I were ready to give up but the consultant psychotherapist persuaded us to persevere. At the next session we had a fiery trio improvisation freely expressing our feelings about Mrs E.'s suicidal attempt. Mrs E.'s were guilty, Mr E.'s sad and then turned to angry feelings which were broken off by his wife (I said she could give the sign to stop) and mine were frankly furious. Mrs E. then discharged herself, kept on attending joint sessions as an outpatient, and for the next three months that my records stretch she gradually took over some of the chores and mothering at home and decided to look for a part-time job. Mr E.'s increased expression in music, going from rigid ostinato drum beats to expressive rhythms and sad and sombre melodies on the melodica, was followed by a firmer attitude to his wife about spending and keeping the sex between them. He also felt able to begin to express normal irritation and despair in the sessions at his wife's inability to take over the full quota of chores. Mrs E. no longer saved all her aggression for uncontrollable explosive quarrels followed by suicidal attempts to escape the backwash. She began to meet his despairing feelings by defending heself verbally. During the eight months that my records last there was a real attempt to reshape the marriage. Mr E. was beginning to realise that giving presents could not be a substitute for giving of himself and his feelings to his wife. The couple talked things over more, went out dancing from time to time, had more social life, thought more about the needs of their children and themselves both as individuals, as a couple and a family unit in society.

The joint session

The effects of taking a joint session can be quite disturbing to the therapist. When he finds that one partner is using him as a club to bludgeon the other with at home, when he senses that there is a collusive curtain of silence drawn over cetain aspects of the couple's life, when he feels that one partner is withholding valuable information for fear of the other's reaction – he can find the going difficult. The music, with its honesty, is a wonderful relief and can tell him a great many things that the words avoided.

If he can possibly work with a co-therapist of the opposite sex he will find his work much easier, in that he can tune in mainly to one partner plus the couple, instead of being torn apart by having the unconscious emotions of both clients meeting and warring inside himself.

Just as a dissonant semi-tone interval can be mollified by adding a harmonising third tone, the presence of the therapist can form the triad which makes the dynamic experiencing of the couple's music possible. By holding the basic root of the chord, he can sometimes enable them to play out the dissonances and find their own natural resolutions. But it is not always easy.

19. Private practice

There are certain advantages to the music therapist working in his own private practice as against being a member of the staff of an institution. First of all, he can work as he pleases and will have no clashes in treatment approach with other therapists working with the same patient. He will have no travelling expenses, he can earn more money and he can fit clients in at times which are convenient to both him and them. As a rule his music therapy will be the only treatment being given; so he will see more clearly the effects of his work, instead of having to consider whether the stimulus to improvement might be due to the art therapist, drama therapist, psychotherapist, the chemotherapy, the electro-convulsive therapy, the social worker or the industrial therapy. He can create his own individual atmosphere in his therapy room without the institutional smell and coldness.

There are also disadvantages. Home – if he works at home – is no longer the little sanctuary where he can shed all his problems. He will not have the stimulation, support and cross-fertilisation of ideas of the therapeutic team and because of this would do well to join a working group which has regular case discussions, like those run by the Institute of Religion and Medicine. Regular contact with some of his colleagues to pool knowledge, ideas and experience will be helpful too. He may find it difficult to get medical coverage as a large number of clients are not registered with a G.P. Other clients, though registered with a G.P., wish to keep medicine well away from the area of magic where they have filed music therapy. They are quite baffled by the idea that the music therapist would like them to have a physical check-up with their doctor to exclude the possibility of an organic source of their trouble. Often they are even unwilling to give the music therapist their doctor's name and address.

A combination of private practice and institutional work is most interesting and gives the therapist experience with the widest range of problems and the understanding of how these are interlinked.

Preventive work is most meaningful when the therapist has experience with what the alternative could be.

PREMISES

The music therapy room may either be away from home, in a suitable rented room, or it can be a room in the home. It should be situated so as to cause minimum annoyance to the neighbours and household. A ground floor or basement room, where the piano and percussion sounds travel downwards into the cellar or ground, can be more easily soundproofed than a room with another beneath it. It should be large enough for groups or for movement sessions but small enough for a feeling of intimacy. A high ceiling increases the heating bills but a false ceiling could be built to cut down both noise and heat loss. Windows should be double glazed in a flat or semi-detached house, with adequate alternative ventilation. It is useful to have a waiting area outside the therapy room but out of earshot of speech even if not of music. As long as the therapist uses only music, live and recorded, and words in his treatment, he needs no kind of licence. If he wishes to use machines and massage then a licence is necessary, but this is unusual.

FURNITURE AND EQUIPMENT

Carpeting cuts down on the resonance and is inconvenient if the therapist is working with young children, but it is pleasant for movement and group relaxation and also for casually sitting round on the floor. Perhaps a large carpet square, which can be rolled away when children come, would be the best. A piano and piano stool or chair are essential, also a reclining chair for the client and an upright chair for the therapist, placed so that he has full eye contact. He will need somewhere to keep the instruments. I use pegboard and hooks on the wall to hang up some of the smaller instruments; I also have hinge-topped window seats. A record player and shelf for records, tape recorder, music stand and music cabinet are also necessary. Useful, though not essential, is a tether ball hanging from the ceiling by a cord and pulley. An office corner is convenient for keeping records and case notes and possibly a telephone which can be unplugged or taken out during sessions.

INSTRUMENTS

Besides the piano, the more simple instruments the music therapist has, on which the novice can make a pleasant sound at once, the better. He could start with a tom-tom on three legs and a cymbal on a stand with a soft-headed beater and a wire brush, and add, as soon as possible, a xylophone. Melodicas, tambourines and chime bars would come next. After that he might add home-made clappers, a bamboo guiro (a South American rasp), claves and maracas. Finally triangles, temple bells, cow bells, Chinese blocks, bongos, Moroccan pottery drums, a kalimba, tambour and Chinese gong would add variety to the auditory experience. Delicate instruments which have to be tuned, such as harps, the violin family, lutes, lyres, guitars, psalteries and chordal dulcimers I find unsuitable for spontaneous expressive therapy. If the client specifically wishes to learn to play and tune one of these instruments, that is another matter. In any case if she is learning the instrument she will be buying her own so that she can take it home to practise. Otherwise the therapist is faced with the prospect of enduring their being played out of tune (which I believe to be anything but therapeutic) or spending valuable therapy time retuning innumerable musical instruments and replacing broken strings instead of reserving the time for tuning the client.

DECORATION

It is my opinion that the therapy room décor should be fairly neutral in tone to fit in with any mood. My room has an olive green carpet, natural wood cupboards, white ceiling and walls and ivory blinds. To accentuate a particular mood I have spotlit blinds in each of the seven colours of the spectrum. I pull down a red or a blue to emphasise a particular feeling. During the relaxation the blind is lit from behind to give a glowing effect. Lighting should be practical but capable of being reduced to encourage lowering the threshold of consciousness when this is needed. Flowers are indispensable as symbols of the unfolding self. Too many pictures hung round the room set the atmosphere in one key; but a softboard area, for pinning up clients' pictures, ephemeral matters of interest or beauty allows for change and flexibility of mood.

Two practical matters which need attention are fire precautions and an insurance which covers the therapist in case a client should have an accident on the premises.

CLIENTS

The music therapist can either decide what kind of clients he would like to have and work out a plan for getting in touch only with them, or he can spread a wide net and see which way the practice develops. It is more interesting not to plan everything. Clients come to the therapist in curious ways. One, who turned out to live only two stops away, I met while I was lecturing on music therapy at an International Festival of Yoga and Esoteric Sciences in Switzerland. Another happened to read my advertisement in a weekly paper while he was in Berlin.

There are three main ways of getting in touch with clients. The first, and simplest, is by referral from doctors, psychiatrists, psychotherapists, colleagues and friends. These people will give the therapist a background picture of the client and also prepare the client for the kind of work which the therapy entails. The next best way is through giving talks and writing articles and books. This way there is no one to provide an objective background picture but at least the client herself knows something about music therapy and understands what kind of work is involved. These clients are usually highly motivated. The last and most unsatisfactory way of attracting clients is by advertisement. At present the public at large does not know what music therapy is. A reasonably priced advertisement cannot give enough space for an adequate explanation – I am even having trouble in this book. If the therapist sticks to minor publications aimed at readers with certain clear-cut disabilities, he will be on safe ground and the response will be from people in genuine need of therapy. However, with the replies from readers of the media for the general public, he is in the jungle. He – and more so if the therapist is a she – will meet with an astonishing variety of misconceptions about his calling. Large numbers of male readers imagine that it is a cover term for some deviate professional sexual activity. Indeed it was some consolation to me to learn that even a craftsman French Polisher with a sign to that effect in his window had had similar responses, Advertising in the most impeccable journals is no protection from such callers. With practice the therapist will be able not only to discourage those who are not looking for music therapy but also to do it with good humour and equanimity. They are people in trouble, even if they are not aware of it. However, lady therapists may think it worth paying extra for a box number in their advertisements, or stipulating "Ladies only" in order to avoid this problem.

Some publications ask for the advertisement and ensuing leaflets to be passed by the Advertising Association who will forward a copy of the British Code of Advertising Practice on request. The important paragraph is B25 stating "Advertisements should not contain any claim (directly or by implication) to extirpate any ailment, illness, disease or symptom of ill-health." (In my dictionary it said that an extirpator is an implement for weeding. I was glad I was not to be one of those.) The Advertising Association also asked me for two letters, containing opinions about my work, by two consultant psychiatrists.

When he has clambered over these hurdles, the music therapist will find that 40 per cent of the clients who make appointments in response to his advertisement fail to arrive. It is useful to have some written work or instrumental practice ready for these occasions. However, some well-motivated clients do slip through and by working successfully with them the therapist will find that in time they bring others and gradually his practice will build up so that advertising becomes unnecessary.

PAYMENT

If, like many musicians, he is useless at keeping accounts, the therapist can ask for payment after each session. It saves a lot of trouble. What he loses in dignity he gains in peace of mind from not worrying about overdue accounts or keeping track of invoices and receipts. It also prevents clients from expressing negative transference by protracted witholding of fees. However affluent the client the therapist should not begin treatment without first coming to a clear agreement about payment. This breaks the taboo about discussing money and puts the relationship on a healthy and realistic footing.

What about clients who cannot pay? The music therapist will have to decide whether he will take people in need for less than his usual fee. If their treatment is going to make them more able to earn money, it is sensible to allow them a period of time in which to produce the fees. Personally I do not think that it is right, psychologically, for any client to have treatment for nothing. Something should be given as a token valuation of the work and contribution to the music therapist's worldly needs, however little. In this way the client is still a giver as well as a receiver. I find this more dignified.

THE SESSIONS

How long should a session be? I aim to work for fifty minutes and have a ten-minute break between clients when I can write notes, get out the next client's notes and generally re-orient myself. Preliminary sessions usually take longer so I like to book them so they can overlap into unbooked time. Group sessions take ninety minutes.

At the first session it is useful to have a questionnaire covering basic facts of history which the therapist can read from and on which he can record answers. This does not stop him from being able to ask open-ended questions later on but it does help him to tether his thinking during a period in which he is wide open to external impressions and obliquely using all his intuitional and receptive functions. It also enables him to make full use of the bonus of anonymity.

How many sessions should be booked in a day? Some therapists never give more than five or six. Others have started at 8 a.m., are still hard at it at 11.55 p.m. and seem to thrive on it. But the therapist must be fair to himself and his clients and his family, if he has one. He needs time to replenish his vitality. When he has decided what his limit is he should stick to it as far as possible and not be tempted to overstrain himself.

What about holidays? It is wise for the music therapist in private practice to take periodic breaks three times a year when he sees no clients at all. The work is very taxing and regular holidays prevent staleness. He should seek for fresh air, fresh food, good company and beautiful strengthening impressions.

RECORDS

Music therapy is new enough for every working music therapist to be doing unique research. The therapist will find that a box file and hole puncher are useful for filing questionnaires and subsequent records of sessions with dreams and improvisation imagery. These, together with tape recordings of musical work, will come in useful in preparing case discussions, research material, talks, articles, papers, books and so on.

LENGTH OF TREATMENT

Clients are seen weekly, sometimes fortnightly and occasionally monthly. The decision to terminate the treatment lies with the client. Some clients need only a single consultative session, some need a few months' treatment, others need supportive therapy which may take several years, but this is something which is discussed freely between the therapist and client or the child or subnormal patient's parents.

CLOTHES

Clothes should be chosen to make the therapist feel as much at ease as possible. Some therapists would not be seen dead in anything other than a good dark suit and immaculately laundered cotton shirt. But for the others clothes should be easy to move in, comfortable and giving a feeling of relaxation that will communicate itself to the client. For men the polo-necked jumper and trousers are more appropriate than a suit. Many women will find that slacks are most convenient and offer the most freedom. In private practice the therapist may feel the need of some exterior mark of authority when working at home. I wear my graduate badge of the British Society for Music Therapists.

MUSIC AND THERAPY

The private practice may consist of music therapy clients and music pupils. The therapist will have to experiment as to whether mixing the two gives him pleasant variety or a nasty case of role confusion. In the latter case, he could arrange to be either therapist or teacher for specified days or part-days, possibly wearing slightly different clothes. Personally I find it quite a difficult change of role. To change from teacher to therapist is easier but from therapist to teacher is quite a jolt.

20. Music therapy with a private client

It is difficult to construct a clear picture of the inner progress of a course of analytical music therapy from brief progress notes. The inability to share the vital experience of our musical improvisations and the music behind the talk and the silences is another problem. However, perhaps these notes on two cases, one of a private client in this chapter and the other of a hospital out-patient (whose improvisations were all taped) in the next, may give you some idea of how the work can develop.

CASE NOTES

Thelma was a small, attractive brunette of 23 married to an executive called Edgar; she was studying singing and piano. They had been married one year, her parents were alive; she had a poor relationship with her mother who was described as having fluctuating moods. There was an elder sister and a brother. Thelma had had moods of depression since she was at secondary school. She was a poor sleeper, waking early, and had bitten her nails since she was seven. She was referred to me by a colleague who knew her husband who said she was behaving in a disturbed manner. I asked her to see her G.P. for a general checkup but she declined.

Session 1

Thelma seemed rather confused and excited, frequently breaking off sentences and changing the subject. She had made Edgar twist her arm by shouting that he had no feelings, then experienced some relief of tension in hitting him. Fear of her anger being like her mother's outbursts (she described one attempted attack on her, as a child, by her mother with a breadknife) had made her seek help. She cried, saying it was a pity for Edgar. Talked about a feeling of being "put down" by school, parents and depressions. I tried to persuade her to improvise this feeling but she couldn't. I tried to make her do a Door in the Wall improvisation on "Why I resent Edgar" which she said she did. She couldn't. She said that when she was depressed she felt that static electricity came to her from everything. She was no longer freely expressive in singing, she said.

Comment: When a patient absolutely cannot bring herself to play, the therapist can switch his attention to the music in the words – here desperation – and the rhythm which was jerky like the actions of a panicky trapped animal.

Session 2

(5 days later). Thelma came early as I was fitting a new electric plug. She launched into outer/inner reality experiences with electricity at home. Fuses were going bang all over the house and the ghost of her grandmother walked. Her face was very excited and strange when she spoke of this. She produced an interesting dream the initial association of which was the memory of being left alone on Sunday evenings while her parents were at church. (She was very much afraid of the dark and electric shocks.) In the dream the living-room light fused and went out with a bang. She lit two candles to light the room. She half-shut one window to prevent the candles being blown out, but the wind blew it open. It was eerie and dark and the window wouldn't shut and latch. She opened the door, the hall light flickered, she ran all over the house and saw that the lights were flickering. The house was somehow the present one and yet also her grandmother's house. I asked her to be the Eerie Darkness in sound while I played her. She resisted doing this improvisation for some time but finally did and felt that the Eerie Darkness was chasing me (her) all over the house. During this music she had a vivid memory of being small, standing at the top of the stairs at her grandmother's and hearing the heavy steps of someone terrifying coming up to get her. This made a very strong impression on her, she was "in it" like someone who has just woken from a dream.

She overvalued her husband's control and thinking, despising her own capacity for feeling too often used only for emotional explosions. I wondered if she were not carrying some of his feelings and overloading her fuses and letting him do her thinking. They needed to be two whole separate conscious individuals like the two lighted candles. She "killed" my sentences repeatedly by butting in fiercely. I asked her if she were trying to make me violent and twist her arm by not paying me the fee last week. She concentrated more this week, worked on herself and looked better.

Session 3

(A week later). Thelma felt energetic and her teacher had said that she hadn't sung so well in years. She brought a dream about visiting her ex-boy-friend Tom in his council house, meeting his father who greeted her pleasantly but she felt he was not pleased. Children were having a sports day on a green surrounded by a wall two bricks high. Thelma's mother was there and Thelma felt inhibited and foolish with her watching. I said I thought I was the inhibiting mother watching the music of her feelings. Next she told me that she felt that marriage was a weight, that she felt the responsibility for Edgar's feelings. He was over a decade older than she. She had had an increase in sexual feelings for other men. We improvised with her being Freedom and me Marriage. She felt my sanctimonious music was stopping her from being free but her xylophone music was marvellous. We exchanged roles and she felt that her marriage was her conscience.

Comment: This increase in sexual feeling is a frequent occurrence during music therapy, especially where the feeling towards the partner is blocked by an unconscious experiencing of him as a parent.

Session 4

A very long session. Thelma had written down her thoughts about marriage which we discussed. She told me that Edgar had had a breakdown when his former girl-friend let him down. The dream about Tom, not sufficiently attended to, had continued in three more dreams in which he figured. In the third dream she had seen him and been titivating in a mirror and had found that only her sad eyes needed attention. I suggested that I was the mirror showing her her sad eyes whereupon she sobbed as if her heart would break and I let her experience this grief to the full. She had known Tom for three years, she had always loved him but pushed the feelings away and married Edgar for security when she was depressed. At first I felt real pain in her crying but after a while it was as if she were begging me to unlock the prison and I said it was she who had the key not I and she must act. She decided to talk to Tom about it. She came right through the experience of her grief and spent several minutes making up her face in the bathroom before leaving in a self-possessed manner.

Comment: This was a tremendous cathartic experience. Had Thelma not been a musician I would have contained her emotion in music but as a musician this would probably have switched on her thinking and broken the complete experiencing of the emotion. As it was I relied on the holding power of my "inner music". (See Chapter 23.)

Session 5

Thelma had talked with Edgar and shown him her poems and writing for the first time saying how rotten she felt and "Help! Help!". She had shown him a side of herself that she had not exposed before. She had seem Tom and talked about her feelings and decided that the only right thing was to separate from both men and find out about herself. I said that there was a rule of "no change under therapy" because it was difficult to work at change internally if there were radical external changes. She said it would not be for six weeks at least. I wondered whether the wish for outer separation was in place of the needed inner separation. We studied a dream where Edgar and she were in the back of a car driven by her parents and as Edgar talked she said, "Shut up! Don't let the parents know what you are teaching me." We discussed her lack of early sex instruction and how Edgar had taunted her saying, "You sing like a virgin." We did two Emotional Investment improvisations. She improvised "Tom", slim, one-sided manageable music, and then "Edgar", very sincere, gentle, tender music with much more real emotion and a feeling of awe and "what comes next?". She said she was "very fond" of Edgar. She said that she had become more responsive to colour.

Comment: The release of emotion often brings a clearer perception of the outer world and its beauties. At this session Thelma insisted on playing the piano and letting me play the instruments.

Session 6

(A week delayed due to the strike.) She had been joking with Tom when their fellow students were there but alone with him she could not communicate until their music had dispersed some of the emotion. We spent some time on a dream in which she was in Machynlleth Station waiting for a connection to Barmouth. (Her father was Welsh.) It was a beautiful day with blue sky and fleecy white clouds. At the top of the road running under the tracks Tom was coming towards her meaning to say it wouldn't work but he couldn't say it, instead he embraced her and she gave in. We then improvised two endings. In the first she tore herself away, got on the train for Wales with Edgar, they looked back and couldn't see Tom. This left her with a feeling of peace. In the other Tom and she got on the train for London and embraced, this left her with feelings of courage and energy. We discussed the association of Edgar with her father and what the road under the tracks might mean.

Session 7

Thelma happily talked about Edgar then said she partly wanted to leave him to find her own independence. We discussed the possibility of doing this while staying where she was. Tom had said that he would need time – at least two years – but thought that she should leave Edgar. I could not get her to play, she kept balking. Finally I said that she was making me feel like an impotent child and had anyone made her feel like that and was she passing on the message to me? Yes, she had come to a stop in the singing class and her teacher had told her exactly what to do and she felt terribly frustrated like a child. We discussed Up and Down parent/child pattern relationships. We tried to play Being Equals on xylophone and chime bars. But first she reacted by playing high when I played low then she got scared and became submissive and copied me. At the end she said that she always let Edgar work out her musical interpretations. As she was going she said anxiously that we had not decided what to do about Tom and Edgar. I said that I was sure that she was perfectly capable of making her own decision when she was ready but what we were doing now was to help her to experience her feelings about the whole situation.

Session 8

Thelma was wearing a smock, looking quite pregnant and very happy and her face all of one piece. She had got on very well with Edgar and decided that she didn't have to leave home to be independent. She had seen Tom and they had worked at some music together and she had made him a present of a tiny home-made animal for his birthday. We did an improvisation of a Door in a Wall marked "Independence" and she went through it into her music room at home and was looking through her diary and dates as if bringing the music into other areas. We improvised Child and she first played stereotyped childish music imagining that she was a boy with building bricks and then played more emotional music feeling the excitement of perhaps after all being able to be the mother of a baby with Edgar as the father. She was feeling capable and happy,

Edgar was pleased too, and we arranged that she should have one further follow-up session in five weeks.

Session 9

Thelma looked very attractive and more mature. The relationship with Edgar was good. She was still feeling love for Tom but had used too much energy in trying to compute what his feelings for her might be instead of talking about her own. She had bought herself a tape recorder to hear her singing – possibly a resolute stand to be her own interpretive critic or even music therapist. We improvised on an old dream of insects getting into the bath which seemed to point to early guilt over body sensations. Her singing was now free and fine. She felt that she was aware of her feelings now and could pour them into the music. She had been back to her parents' home with Edgar and felt how insecure her mother was, always trying to placate others instead of being real. We agreed that this should be the last session but that she could come back at any time and she asked me for a copy of the notes because she felt that so much had happened so quickly and she wanted to think it all through.

Comment: I felt that there was plenty more that we could usefully look at but Thelma wanted to stop there and I agreed in spite of my feeling that she was avoiding something. Six weeks later Edgar wrote to me about the therapy: "I think the biggest difference that therapy has made is that Thelma knows herself much better or, as she puts it, she can better face up to herself. This has given her the confidence to discuss her feelings more fully (she always did say what she *thought*!) and has given us a much more realistic basis on which to face the other problems. Possibly as a result, the hysterical outbursts which punctuated our married life every two or three weeks seem to have vanished. Thelma adds that she is now much better able to make friends with people at [her place of study] than formerly.

"The problem which therapy cannot answer is Thelma's need for freedom, of which she seems to have become increasingly aware during your work together. This appears to go much further than a conflict of feeling between Tom and myself, but is rather a need to find a greater inner freedom. It looks as if we may decide to live apart, at any rate for the time being."

I was hoping that Thelma was going to be able to find this independence within the marriage, and indeed she may do this eventually. But the couple were now seriously facing their real

174

difficulties, able to talk more freely and honestly about feelings and to try to work something out together which had been completely impossible in the state in which Thelma was at the start of the sessions.

Thelma's music was rather timid and controlled in the sessions but it sufficed to allow her to get in touch with powerful inner images and feelings which she then used in between sessions in writing, discussing, and in her music which became much more of a real vehicle of her own individual expression. Her own work with her feelings and thinking in between sessions was a great help to her progress.

21. Notes on a hospital patient's music therapy

PSYCHIATRIST'S COMMENT BEFORE MUSIC THERAPY
"Kevin D., aged 32

"This man was referred to a Consultant Neurologist with a history of pains in the neck and left arm following flu. He had been on and off work for several months. No sign of neurological disease was found and the Neurologist advised early return to work as he felt the patient was getting introspective. At a subsequent psychiatric interview the patient said that he had at times felt sick while in a car and had felt giddy a few weeks before the attack of flu.

"The patient was referred to the Psychiatric Out-Patients' Clinic by his GP as no progress was being made. The doctor reported the patient as feeling light-headed and in a haze and 'full of smiles complaining of headache and trembling'. He had been in and out of work. At his first interview he described such anxiety symptoms as a feeling 'As if going out . . .' when he would shake his head and tell himself that he would be all right in a minute. He could not sit still in a football stand, and in the market he felt 'Let me out'. He felt inclined to bad temper and said that he easily became giddy. He had pains across his back and the back of his neck, headaches, depression, a fear of dying which he woke up with in the night. At his worst he had felt 'I could sling myself in the canal'. Various medications were tried but with only moderate relief though there was some relief of his depression. Three months later he was seen by a Consultant Orthopaedic Surgeon who could find no organic cause for the persistent back pain. The following month he was made redundant at work and steps were taken to get him into the ITO. [The Industrial Training Organisation is a factory employing psychiatric patients who are not yet ready to undertake ordinary commercial employment.] After he had been attending ITO regularly for a month the back pain was getting worse. He was referred to the music therapist the following month. He attended music therapy once weekly and the music therapist sent me regular reports of the content of the sessions and of his progress. He continued to attend

Notes on a hospital patient's music therapy

the Psychiatric Out-Patients' Clinic at intervals of a few months for general impressions and review of medication. He also continued to attend the ITO regularly."

WORKING WITH KEVIN

From the beginning working with this patient was an extraordinary experience. It was as if our verbal exchange was expressed within a limited spectrum of black, white and – say – red. The intercommunication only reached its full multi-coloured flowering through his dreams and vivid emotive unconscious images. The emotion contained in these was released in his playing and expressed more fully and fed back to him consciously through mine. To play an improvisation with Kevin was like lifting a man up to look over a high wall. At first one took part in the experience usefully but partially and blindly. Later one could share his astonishing picture of the hidden part of the operation. These images had then to be related dynamically to his life tasks. Much of the treatment was a process of re-education. He had to learn to tolerate and express real feelings, however painful, rather than hand them imperturbably over to doctors as dissociated ready-made symptoms. These had to be carefully decoded and turned into emotional experiences which we could share. His early life with kindly, conscientious but not empathetic mother substitutes seemed to have taught him that feelings about his little troubles and stresses of life could not helpfully be shared. Physical symptoms, however, produced instant tangible concern in the form of the symbolic sympathy of pills, potions and powders. Small wonder then that he gave up even experiencing the feelings in favour of producing symptoms, building up a personality on what is medically termed conversion hysteria.

To a certain extent his musical expression was also contained within a limited spectrum. I felt the counter-transference very strongly and gave him back the powerful feelings that were not otherwise admitted to his conscious realisation. He gradually began to accept them from me; in music, first, he gave them back and then in words. As we worked, I had the feeling that he was coming into focus as a man. The original rather hopeless, helpless atmosphere of the verbal communications, and timid shaking of the maracas, gave way to word patterns that seemed to have real bones in them. His music became more defined, it gained in confidence and a feeling of direction. Occasional surges of emotional colour on the cymbals alternated with curious two-instrument episodes. How he managed this

177

was often hard to imagine, I couldn't see him from behind the grand piano.

Hearing the play-back of the tape recording was a very important part of the session. At first Kevin would experience psychosomatic symptoms as the symbolic sound expression of his emotions was reflected back to him. Later on he could listen with enjoyment, relating the sounds to the inner experiences and feeling without any physical distress.

Besides his weekly music therapy this out-patient was having chemotherapy from the psychiatrist whom he saw infrequently and a holding base in working at the Industrial Training Organisation. I sent in weekly reports to his psychiatrist and we met now and then but I was never in touch with the ITO for practical reasons. I was not entirely happy about this as patients tend to view non-communicating therapists unconsciously as quarrelling parents and play one off against the other. I call this "playing Daddies and Mummies" with the communication between the therapists only being carried by "patient post". It is a situation ordinarily to be avoided.

THE SESSIONS
Session 1
Kevin was 32, married, with a son Tom, of five. His wife, Clara, was a housewife. He had been off work for 14 months but was employed at the ITO factory in the afternoons at work therapy. He had been a mechanical engineer. Kevin had a jolly, fat face (rather reminiscent of a baby) and, in fact, he looked to me somehow like a big baby sitting dejectedly waiting to be picked up. He told me about his back pains. I put my hands on the spot where he described the pains as feeling like "two circles". They were located exactly where his breasts would be if they were at the back. From here he said the pains went up his neck and throbbed in his forehead making his mind "wander" as he put it. I asked if anything had ever happened to him which he had felt as a metaphorical stab in the back. He told me that his mother had left home when he was four. This was the same age as his son Tom was when Kevin's illness came on. It looked as if there was some identification with his son which made him feel unconsciously that it was unsafe to be away from home.

We improvised "Mountain Ascent". I played the piano and he played the drum, rather timidly. Afterwards he said the climb was easy at first then difficult in spasms and he gave up from fatigue. I made him do a second ascent. This time he chose to play a maracca, rather lightly, and he said that he got to the top of the mountain but shut his eyes. He has a fear of heights, also a fear of death as going to sleep and not waking up. He talked freely about himself, how his father had been afraid of death and given three months to live if he refused to have an operation. (He had it.) The thought of not knowing his mother bothered him. "YOU could be my mother," he exploded.

Session 2

Kevin had done some research on his mother, a taboo subject throughout the family. Clara had thought that I talked sense and that he was nervous when she was away. He'd felt a bit stirred up and dizzy. We improvised "Falling Off a Cliff". He drummed, cymbal was fall and then I played bass rumbles and he was silent. "Just darkness." His foster father had frightened him with bogeymen. We played "Cave Watch" and out came two eyes like points of fire, then a green dragon breathing fire emerged twice and went back in. We talked about the two fiery eyes and the two back pains and how sad and angry he must have felt on the dark morning when he found his mother gone. He wept. His playing was quite emotional.

Session 3

The back pains had gone but instead he had pains in his neck and shoulders and a "wandering" feeling in his head. He had been angry and irritable with Tom, and with a guest, and very involved with a TV boxing match. He assured me that *his* wife was very capable and would ring him if she couldn't cope with anything to do with Tom. He must have felt guilty about his mother. We improvised Splitting (see Chapter 14), with me playing "Wandering" and him "Struggle" (to keep going). He played quite fiercely then when we exchanged roles his "Wandering" was really angry. When he heard the play-back he got the back pains and his hands were gripping the couch in rage.

Session 4

Kevin wanted to try doing mornings in the ITO. I encouraged him. We improvised "The Morning After Mother Left", there was fear and sadness at what would become of his brethren and some anger. We improvised his "Anger At Mother" as if he were arguing with her on the drums. He was very fierce. I put her case forcefully on the piano. Afterwards he said he felt bitter and angry and verbalised the whole argument. There was a conspiracy of silence about it throughout the family, he had never been able to be angry with anyone about it before.

Session 5
He was full of how he couldn't get permission to do mornings, he went on and on about what the ITO woman had said about music therapy. I suddenly realised that he was trying to make me express his anger for him but I didn't bite. He became more genuinely annoyed than before. We improvised on his despairing feeling about his illness and his hopeful feeling. Twice he let the hopeful feelings be overcome then the two feelings went into a terrible battle and he felt sleepy and "dropped away". I suggested that this was internal parents quarrelling.

Session 6
No back pains, just a twinge and lots of loading at work but headaches and neck pains and feelings of "going out on my feet", and a feeling that something would happen to his son Tom. I pounced on this, explaining the possible unconscious desire behind the fear. We improvised a Splitting of "Something"/"Tom". He visualised a scene where Tom was going up and down the garden path then ran out up the road. Kevin called, a bus ran over the boy but he was all right. Then I made him BE the bus in music and as he played he felt "I must get on' and then he was the driver trying to stop the bus running over a crowd of people, fighting to stop it. I played it back and it was evidently a very emotional experience, he could tell which bit meant what. Much more aggression and emotion in speech.

Session 7
Kevin spoke of good things he'd like to do for children and his treatment of his son. He complained of a claustrophobic feeling in shops. We improvised a Splitting of "Kevin"/"Shop" (me) and he got more and more agitated and smashed all windows and doors and then could breathe at peace. Then as "Shop" he felt hard and uncaring and then squeezed Kevin (me) in sound. He spoke of his awareness of a war of good and bad inside himself, of a part thinking, "Why should they have it? I never did" and another part wanting to do good.

Session 8
(Fortnight later.) He had been appropriately aggressive to people at

180

hospital who had messed up his appointments. On holiday he had got the feeling of going to be dragged off the walls of Carisbrooke Castle. He played "Dragged Down"/"Kevin" (me) and he felt that a great hole in the earth was pulling him down and pushing him along passages against blind ends then suddenly he was out in the fresh air and didn't know how. Could it be a birth memory? He described a *déjà vu* experience by the sea in the Isle of Wight feeling "excited and overwhelmed" and "in my own world". This seemed valuable so I asked him to recall it and picture it in sound which he did very beautifully with xylophone glissandi.

Sessions 9 and 10

Realisation of his having to prove himself. Trying to apply relaxation while playing. Able to be angry at work and felt splendid. Hopes to try for a full day at ITO soon.

Session 11

Had had a queer week feeling "split between body and mind". Also standing at bus stop feeling he was going to fall over in front of the bus and then a dead feeling. I made him play "The Thing that he waited anxiously for before he crossed the road". Angry xylophone and drum music. He was a big mechanical "Thing" with great big jagged teeth which was going to eat him up once and then again and then spit him out. This was said with forceful expression. He played "Body"/"Mind" (me) and played free, relaxed music, "felt nothing", was just moving his arms. Then he played "Mind" and improvised taut little phrases. He said that he had felt that he didn't want to come today in case I said he would have to feel worse. I said I thought that he was experiencing me as the awful mother who let him have these terrible feelings. He is now feeling the split that gave him the back pains and it is unpleasant.

Session 12

Worry about interview. We improvised "Interview" and he had fierce xylophone getting more and more agitated and then beautiful bells and this was realising that the interviewer was friendly and talking to him. Then we did a Wall and Door marked "The Question I cannot Answer". By counter-transference I played rolling, harplike, solemn chords and he said he got through into a graveyard and he was crawling round the stones pushing aside leaves looking for a name and he didn't know what name. We discussed it being his

181

mother's. He now tolerates his son better and helps him to mend things.

Session 13

Felt "couldn't-care-less", relaxed and concerned about his own work and not so anxiously do-gooding to other comrades. Put his feet on mantelpiece and just sat and was admonished by son. Had listened to music on record player all week and not much TV. Thought he might learn to play the piano. Did "Couldn't-Care-Less" improvisation and he played carefree xylophone. I made fierce provoking bass and he thought "I am doing MY mood" and didn't change then did lovely tambourine trill and bells. He really enjoyed it. We did pentatonic melodica and piano improvisation. He has twice had slight back pains. Shedding burdens consciously.

Session 14 (*4 weeks later*)

Brown and well, had felt more irritable and "don't care what they think" and stuck up for what he believed, even to his father "not like me" and when he was not speaking up had internal arguments. Had had severe neck and headaches in late afternoons. We played "Headache"/"Kevin" and he was entirely IN the feeling, then when I was "Headache" and he was trying to defend himself against the feeling he actually got the headache physically.

Session 15

Looked well, in his face, happy, had had a better week but dull headaches, particularly on Saturday and strong feeling of wanting to run out during the ITO day but they'd given him a better, more responsible job and been quite different to him. We played "Running Out" (him)/"Staying At Work", he was tremendously dynamic and played at length on the drum as never before. When we switched I was freaky on the piano and he felt such a temptation to join me but managed to overcome it. I think this IS the feeling keeping him off work, which has now dared to come to light.

Session 16

Had been better in the mornings. Nightmares about dying. Dizzy feeling bending over in the garden. Tests had proved physically normal. He thought about death and his heart beat fast. He believed in God and prayed a childhood prayer every night. Didn't go to church, could pray anywhere. Didn't feel that dead relatives were near. Gone. Used to think he'd see Grandma's ghost. Never did. Hated funerals especially when the body is lowered into the earth. Played "Dying" and felt that he was sinking the way he felt in first illness and then when dead was in a dark room searching for a friendly face and none came. Very affected by playback.

Session 17

Had felt awful, all shaky and trembly and even had back pains again. All his talk was about his conscientious feelings versus "wanting to go" feelings at work. He had slept well and no more nightmares. We improvised "Light in the Dark" and he went into the dark room and with a torch saw rows of skulls and then a door and he went out into the fresh air and country and he was peaceful.

Session 18

Looked relaxed again, had bad shakes outside but not inside, angry and "not in control", could now feel like taking the day off but did not need to respond to the feeling. Had come home late and wife had worried about him being run over and he'd said, "I'm afraid of dying – I want to live." There seemed to be a loosening up in family dynamics. He could now talk to his wife as to me about feelings and he didn't bottle things up. We played "In Control", which he found difficult, with me playing "Out of Control", then he played this and really lashed out. Sunday was good. He asked how long the therapy would go on as he was a bit fed up but realised that people had talk-therapy for as long as eight years. I sensed his ambivalent feelings towards me.

Session 19

Had had some really good days and feelings then the bad days felt worse. Had become angry, his wife had ridiculed him and not helped him to express himself and he got hot flushes and bottled it up until his son goaded it out of him. We discussed wife's possible fear of anger in herself and others. Kevin feels as if anger is a "long piece of string" and he could chop only a bit off. We improvised "The Whole Piece of String" but as he did the anger became the inhibiting force and it sounded very constipated. Often planned not going to ITO right up to the gate; now in touch with this wish consciously instead of through symptoms.

Session 20

He had had a repeated dream of someone coming in and standing by his bed. When he was the person in music he was very fierce and bass, when I was the person he played in a light, anxious, chirpy manner. As the person he felt that he wanted to strangle someone. When asked whom, he said, "My mother for leaving my little sister." (He and his wife have decided to find out about his mother.) This image, he said, ties up with him, at 15, trying to strangle himself and being prescribed pills which stopped him wanting to do this. He looks relaxed and more mature. We discussed termination of treatment after he had settled into a new job.

Session 21

Looking relaxed. Very tired after work. Wife understanding. Felt his legs would let him down, or his whole body might but felt guilty about not doing a good day's work. He has subject/object confusion about letting down now. Wanted my address in case he couldn't come to music therapy and might let me down. I gave it to him. Feeling at parties everyone was thinking, "Who the hell is he?" In music he played being in the party and felt how he was when he was going to see his brother for the first time since he had been sent to be brought up in an institution. Then when I was "The Party" and he came in he felt as if he were meeting his father for the first time after the war and what would he think? He felt sad and angry with no one to blame.

Session 22

Had had good Sunday and Monday and thought that he would go and get a job then very bad headache Tuesday and Wednesday. His body had "let him down". He was able to be quite annoyed with me with encouragement, it was all very well for ME, HE had to suffer it. He played "Tuesday"/"Monday" (me), then we changed round and he played "Monday" resolutely against my headachy "Tuesday". He played well and really kept his bit going and actually felt tense and as if the headache were coming on.

Session 23

Had had good hours and bad. Headaches less severe but the awareness of the anger and confusion behind them he called "scrabbling". During these spells people annoyed him by asking if he was all right. Had been upset by three suicidal ITO patients. I said perhaps part

184

of him wanted to kill off his emotions so he identified with them. He said he showed one of them how the machine worked, saying "You must be master of the machine". We played "Scrabbling" and "Peace of Mind" and he had some very angry whacks at me therapist/ mother on the cymbal which he could talk about. Peace of Mind rather restless and he felt it might be better if he took two instruments at once. He added the maraca to the xylophone.

Session 24

Good hours and bad. Told about ITO Manager giving a sniff at music therapy. Had felt scared of first-floor window on fireworks night, grabbed Tom so he couldn't fall out. That night dreamed he was in theatre and felt dizzy, couldn't find his pill then found it and felt OK and on way out noticed that other people coming down the stairs were in triplicate. I said that if he were like that he could be like himself being scared, his boy-self eager and interested, plus his wife/mother caring for him. He improvised "The Force Pulling Him Down" while I played at being him, and the force was a rope that came round his neck and pulled him down to the ground and then held him down with two weights. He felt awful playing it. Then he was the three people and found that he was having terrible arguments all the time. His playing was very violent.

Session 25

Had had a really good week except for a headache on Sunday. He could now play riotous "Tom and Jerry" games with Tom and be the internal caring parent for his anxious self much more this week. Talked a lot about funeral of grandmother, how he knew she was dead from his premonitions. His aunt thought he should not have played that day. We improvised his "Clamp" headache and he felt it wouldn't go.

Session 26

Had had a restless tingling in his body which seemed to say "Go ahead!" and he was afraid of what might "come out" and tried to control it in the early morning. He said if I'd said that my car was outside, "Let's go to Brighton for the day", he'd jump at it. He had been so eager to come and tell me this. He looked well and happy. We split "Tingling"/"Sadness" but his music didn't seem sad. Later I asked for all the anger because the back pains had reappeared on Monday, and then his feelings about Brighton. He played very angrily, two instruments at once, and then felt he was knocking on a door marked "The Good Times at Brighton".

Session 27
Had felt better and had no pains then worse and had them, very tired. Felt "choked up" coming to see me when three jobs had come up at ITO. We played "Choked Up" and he felt "I'm not doing it right", and told how he didn't put on the kettle at home when told and hadn't done anything to help his little brethren who had been taken to an institution when his father was called up. I played "Aunt issuing curt commands" and he played back angrily then when I played gentle requests he took his time and answered quite happily and gently back.

Session 28
The psychiatrist had said that he and I and the ITO manager would have a meeting about Kevin and if we all agreed Kevin could go back to work. (Somehow we never did!) Kevin said he realised it would be hard but felt ready. He described a fight at work which he, being in charge then, had prevented by parting the men furiously and making them apologise and make up. Later he related a dream where he was in a room with a circular light, on the outside, and in the centre his wife and another woman (he quickly substituted "person") whom he could not see, were quarrelling and his wife was saying "All right, you take him if you want him." He played as the woman and she was saying "You're not good enough for him." After parting the men he had had a headache.

Session 29
Looked well and relaxed, had had pins and needles and back pains and thought he'd die before Christmas like his father had thought before his illness. Aunts had been quarrelling and fussing. He said, "It gives me the needle." I made him musically give me (as aunts) the pins and needles and he did very fiercely and ended up by actually having not only the pins and needles feeling but also the back pains! In a fish and chip shop everything "got on top of me" and he wanted to go out but put all his concentration into conversation and overcame it. I played "Everything" and he felt himself being drawn in, next time he was "Everything" and felt really himself and great. Very vivid playing.
    (I took this session to the case discussion with the Consultant

Notes on a hospital patient's music therapy

Psychotherapist who suggested that Kevin's sexual feelings were unconciously closely linked with his aggression and this brought guilt and self-punishment when he had tried to give me (as aunts) "the needle". I was to explain this to Kevin.)

Session 30

Looked fat, happy and relaxed. I couldn't remember what it was I had to tell him, then when he said, "I put my spoke in..." to a Mr D. in the ITO contradicting him, I told him about the aggression and sexuality being closely associated in his unconscious. Right after this he said how some mothers calmed their babies by masturbating them. He went on to say that when he met a strange girl he always blushed and only when he got talking could he calm down. We improvised "Meeting" and he said it was fear that he might be promiscuous as he imagined his mother was and he had hardly liked to tell me.

Sessions 31 and 32

Felt and looked better. Had helped university student patient to work machines and felt good. Had seen the Disablement Resettlement Officer.

Session 33

We did a ten-minute improvisation. Very lively, different moods, anxiety about a new job came up.

Session 34

Looking well and relaxed. Annoyed at Mr D. at ITO for making him do staff jobs. "Where's my white coat?" he felt like saying. I said it was like him having been the eldest of the three children helping their father. Yes. Feeling of split between body and mind, wanting/ not wanting to work. We played. He said he found it easier to express in music. Wife had thought that on the phone I had sounded younger than he had said and beautiful. I suggested a joint session at the termination to allay her fantasies about the relationship if the psychiatrist agreed. (He did.)

Session 35

Had been having his "heads" and "floating off" because he was so angry and frustrated about not getting a job, a feeling that the Employment Exchange were inefficient. He'd had a dream about being in a holiday camp chalet by a ballroom, turning a tap on and water flowing on and on, no plug and going all over the floor.

187

Finally being given another chalet upstairs. He played "Water" and felt furious "must get out" and when he started wouldn't stop and didn't know where to go. "Like looking for a job?" Yes. He looked very bright and clear, more in focus. Peeved when Mr D. at ITO said "Those other idiots can't be trusted" and had almost walked out. "I was one of them, too," he said.

Sessions 36 and 37
Frustration at trying to get back to work.

Session 38
Had been offered and refused poorly paid job. He had been quite angry, with no headache, pains or pins and needles. We talked about the roles of patient and worker which we then played. As "Patient" he thought, "I don't know how long I can stand this", and as "Worker" was nervous about whether he could do a job, then felt he could. He was angry with Mr D. but I suggested he should rather concentrate on being Manager of his own body and relax it and we tried this in music.

Sessions 39 to 46
In sessions 39 and 40, we used applied relaxation in playing and looked at fears and frustrations about no job coming up. He was more concerned with external reality and less with his symptoms.

It was decided that I should see Kevin for about six sessions after he settled into a new job. Sessions 41 to 46 were rather supportive sessions over troublesome interviews. The impending termination of treatment brought up fears about earlier disastrous terminations of relationships: his mother's disappearance at four, his father's call-up at five and his grandmother's death (she was his first mother-substitute) one year after he left her to live with an aunt.

Session 47
His wife was rather anxious as to whether he would get back to work. He now felt happy to wait. He recounted a striking dream of being on a boat, a coffin was going to be put overboard but the lid slid off and a young person sat up crying. As he rushed forward to wipe away the tears some people slid the lid on and the coffin went irrevocably into the sea. He played very colourfully as the "Crying Corpse" and then was the "People" two pushing the coffin into the sea and one, with himself, trying to hold it back. I said that the Crying Corpse was like himself with his early feelings waking during the therapy and now perhaps he felt that these feelings must go

forever uncomforted. As I said this his eyes were huge and enormously sad like those of a desolate child.

Session 48

He had dreamt several times that he was sliding down an anti-clockwise spiral stairs with a sheer drop to the left and stairs to the right. He always woke up before landing. We improvised on the dream which I asked him to finish satisfactorily. This time when he got to the bottom someone was standing by watching to see him land safely. As he approached the person it kept the distance between them constant and finally vanished. He felt it was his Gran. I pointed out its resemblance also to his therapists but said that with luck we would not disappear so dramatically. We agreed that he should have six sessions after he started his new work to tide him over the feelings about the new experience.

Sessions 49 to 54

He played rhythmically in a spontaneous way for the very first time so that our music was able to share his beat. Here he was expressing his aggression in a positive, energetic way in his work and relationships. By session 54 he had found, and for a fortnight had held, a good job in an understanding engineering firm which specialised in helping people from the ITO to get on their feet. He was able to do quite physically strenuous work without any recurrence of the back pains, and got on well with his fellow workers. The only snag had been that on the day and hour when we usually had our session (I now took him on another evening) he experienced hot and cold flushes and a thuddy headache which did not really disappear until he came to his session the following evening. I felt that these were psychosomatic expressions of transferred feelings about the parents vanishing and leaving him with uncontainable emotions. I was felt to be another kind of letting-down parent. I explained this. It was rejected but the phenomenon ceased nevertheless the next week.

Kevin seemed to me to be a better defined personality at the end of treatment. He was now willing to shoulder and work with his problems and symptoms and accept and express a much greater range of emotion in speech as in music. He seemed to be a more forceful and determined person in his dealings with the world and a warmer and easier man in his home setting. All this showed first in his musical expression. I enjoyed working with Kevin, he was a trier with a difficult personality make-up.

Practical experiences and techniques

PSYCHIATRIST'S COMMENT AFTER MUSIC THERAPY

"Generally Kevin seemed much improved. He appeared more confident and more in touch with himself and others. Alert and cheerful without being euphoric, he was not so bothered by his bodily sensations. The headaches and neckaches were infrequent and when he did experience them he was able to relate them to his current emotional reactions and interpersonal relationships.

He had become a pleasanter person at home: for example he would play cricket with his son instead of moping. He was more patient and tolerant with others, and related how he had helped a young man at the ITO who was learning to use a machine and being a bit stubborn about it.

Soon afterwards, he obtained an engineering job with a firm where the supervision was understanding and helpful. After he had been there a fortnight, he reported that he was enjoying his work, and had in fact done some overtime. He did mention having some headaches which occurred on Wednesdays, the day of the week on which he had formerly had a music therapy session. He occasionally felt depressed. He was sleeping well, and had an excellent appetite. He was enjoying his leisure more, for example he had recently had a game of tennis which he had not played for a long time.

I am convinced that music therapy has played an important part in this man's striking improvement. He himself said that verbal interviews with the music therapist would not have been as beneficial because the music therapy had enabled him to express his feelings better. It is interesting to note that this patient was attending the ITO before he went to music therapy and that his back pains got worse at the ITO (just as they had when he tried to go back to his usual job). After about six sessions of music therapy the pain in the back was diminishing and he was more aware of his emotions.

There are many patients whose persistent physical complaints cause them to be referred from one hospital department to another, and even if they eventually reach the psychiatric clinic much time will have been lost and much damage may have been done in the occupational and domestic spheres. Furthermore these patients may prove difficult to help by interviews which can be given only infrequently. Medication provides some relief but drowsiness and other unwanted effects may occur, and there is the risk of drug dependence. For such patients music therapy may well prove most valuable."

Part Three
Thoughts around music therapy

22. Aims of music therapy

THE MAIN AIM
In considering all the different kinds of clients with all their varying
disabilities, the one overriding aim that is relevant both to working
with the brain-damaged child and the highly intelligent psychiatric
patient, is that of helping the client to achieve her full potential.
It is a large and vague aim, the acceptance of which, however, gives
the music therapist a strong feeling of direction. The aim is more
like the pull going through a magnet, or like living in a district
with a prevailing wind, than striking out for any specific small
hit-or-miss target.

No aim in analytical music therapy
I will now paradoxically state that in analytical music therapy the
therapist should have no aim whatsoever. If he can take a dynamic,
developmental view of the client's psyche, it will gradually become
clear that this has its own aim, relentless as a river. Against this
mainstream have come obstacles forming countercurrents and
stagnant pools. The therapist will endeavour to help the client to
summon the courage to remove these obstacles through applying
her adult mind to revealed childish attitudes frozen into perpetuity
by unexpressed painful emotions. The therapist helps her by provid-
ing a musical container to receive and complement the expression
of her painful emotions and make it safe for her to talk about them
and the memories they evoked afterwards.

Here is an example of this. A Mrs B., an attractive, depressed,
middle-aged woman, was attending my psychodynamic movement
and relaxation group for the first time. She told me first of all that
she could not relax and had to be always "on the go". I wondered
what she was afraid of stopping and experiencing. After dancing
freely to de Falla's *Ritual Fire Dance*, she said, "I want to explode!"
but she felt that she couldn't do this in front of the rest of the group.
In the verbal preamble for the next dance she said, "I can't feel
anything for my daughters; if they are affectionate to me I can't

respond. I just feel nothing." I said that it was possible that her good feelings for her children were covered over with other feelings which she found difficult to acknowledge. She gave me that blank stare which usually means that the therapist has hit the mark but that the client is defending herself against it.

During the next hour, Mrs B. had her first instrumental Group Improvisation session. My colleague Mr O., who took it, said that he was going to give her his full permission to explode. In order to provide a non-threatening containing image for the improvisation he suggested that the group should create a sound picture of a thunderstorm. Mrs B. was given the cymbal on a stand. The music had only just started when Mrs B. really did explode. Magnificently. Cascade upon cascade of shattering metallic sound vibrations broke through her feeling of nothingness. Even Mr O. was a bit anxious for a moment. As the improvisation finished she sat bowed down with her head in her hands while the group improvised "Peaceful Night" music to help to hold and reassure her that she was accepted, explosion and all. When it was over Mrs B. said that she was astonished to find that a tremendous fury against her daughters had welled up as she struck the cymbal; she felt that they were only nice to her because of what they could get from her. She had never believed that she could have such feelings. "I feel so tired I could just drop," she finished. At last she had stopped running away from herself. What my words could not do to convince her, was done by her inner music finding valid and permissible outer expression on the cymbal.

The client who senses that the therapist is on the side of her main aim can stand a great deal of toughness when the therapist bars the way back via some attractive little countercurrent and makes her work against it till it joins the mainstream and breaks through the impeding obstacle.

Any setting of an external aim for the client imposes a limitation on the therapy. In trying to achieve such an aim, valuable developments outside it will be passed by. Also the real work in analytical music therapy lies right in the centre of the client's being. The results, which may vary from the mending of broken relationships, the losing of unpleasant symptoms, the choice of a new career or the finding of a new ability to communicate and make relationships, are on the periphery of his experience. These results are not achieved by being directly aimed at. The therapist is in the position of a hunter with a gun who aims at a rabbit in a field, pulls the trigger, and three wood pigeons fall down dead in the thicket behind him. He can be delighted at the creative way in which the client has been able to use the freed energy but he must give the client credit for the results. For the therapist to choose the direction in which this energy should be used, as a therapy aim, would be to rob the client of her own vital creativity. It could also take from the client her own inner motivation for wanting to have that energy at her disposal and thus stop her from overcoming the obstruction at all.

Even to have as an aim the removal of symptoms can be threatening to a client. A young woman phobic client turned to me in great anguish after seven sessions, when she felt her phobia receding, and said, "Don't cure my phobia too quickly." She knew she needed help to face all her anxieties about activities which the phobia had usefully prevented her from engaging in, before she was prepared to part with it peacefully.

The music therapist spends a considerable amount of time listening to clients just because the results of the analytical music therapy are not experienced in the one-to-one relationship working at the centre, but are in the periphery in the client's private life and outer life relationships. The obstacles and progress here point back to the musical work to be done at the centre. Often the results are wildly different from anything that the therapist could have hoped for.

So from saying that there is one overriding aim to stating that there should be no aim at all, I will veer to the direction of believing that the client and therapist between them produce a mutual aim, with the therapist dominating the direction of the central work and the client that of the periphery.

FUNCTIONS OF THE THERAPIST

1. To be a nodal point

The concept of a therapist being a nodal point came to me while learning to make a glockenspiel. I will explain. To play this instrument one strikes oblong metal plates, which are held on a wooden frame, with beaters. In making the instrument, the metal plates are attached to the frame by having holes bored at one of their nodal points, and being slipped over raised nails, one nail tethering each plate. To find the nodal point, the plate is placed on the frame, sprinkled with metal filings, and tapped with a beater. The area which vibrates most – the anti-node – throws all its filings off on to the two nodal points at either end. One of these is then marked and bored so that the nail can go through it. It was while making my third hole that I thought, "This is what it is to be a music therapist. I am a nodal point. I hold fast to the larger reality and by my stillness allowing her to move, my client lets go and vibrates, communicates feelings and throws off filings." When clients cannot communicate I go back to this image and do less and less and less. And finally more happens.

2. To be a sympathetic string
The sympathetic string is not directly bowed or plucked in an instrument but its vibration enriches the tone. This conception might appear to be contrary to the former yet it is equally necessary. It can be the therapist's vibration in sympathy with a feeling which the client is not yet aware of, and the therapist can bring it to her awareness through music and later words. It can be a vibration which mysteriously gives the client that vital Permission-To-Be which others may have unconsciously or consciously denied her in early life. It can be just that factor which allows the client to take her creative play area out of cold storage, where it has been since her childhood, and turn it into a shared area of creative musical play, having fertilising aspects of both fantasy and reality.

3. To investigate inner music with the client
The therapist is an explorer, with an attitude of curiosity and courage, in the regions of inner space. He endeavours to bring the client's inner difficulties into external reality by means of sound expression which can be felt through the body, listened to through the tape recorder, thought about, discussed, explained, enjoyed and compared with its inner existence. He dares to take the client right through her taboo areas, badlands and volcanic ranges. But only because he, himself, has explored his own first with a guide.

4. To receive and hold treasures and feed them back as necessary
This is something which the therapist needs to be constantly aware of. Sooner or later the client may deposit the treasures of her ability or being with the therapist. It is important to receive them consciously in exactly the words in which they were given. This moment reminds me of the disrobing of a bather prior to her cleansing sea bathe. It is followed by a facing up to her full despair and feeling of unworthiness regarding the undeveloped part of her emotional self. This is the moment for the therapist not to be seduced into sharing the feeling of despair but bit by bit to hand back the treasures.

196

Using the client's own words they come back with the full impact of all their associations which the therapist may or may not be aware of but the client certainly is.

5. To offer, where appropriate, his genuine responses and convictions
A professional musician plays with his whole available self, all that he is goes into the music. It is therefore not possible at the next minute to turn from the piano and become a faceless playing-card being, made that way so as better to receive the projections of clients. Without thrusting his views and values on the client unbid, the therapist should offer her a relationship with a real person, and be prepared to place before the client such of his genuine convictions as he would be prepared to share with anyone outside therapy if challenged. To do less is insulting. This conviction and wholeness of response is something that can either be accepted or rejected but it is a reality against which the client can test herself. However, this is not to say that normal therapeutic reticence is not helpful in assisting the client to achieve her own standpoint. Nor that the need for constant questions about the therapist himself should not be investigated rather than complied with untherapeutically.

6. To stimulate growth
The music therapist must act as a catalyst in situations where exterior frustration is used defensively as a cover for inner constriction. Because music takes place in the creative play area in between inner and outer reality, it can be used to let the client take her first step in actualising a new direction, and breaking down the barriers between thinking, feeling and doing.

7. To survive, with amiable integrity, the client's shadow side
This is the hardest function for a musician to perform. The manifestation of the shadow brings the kind of testing behaviour which provokes feeling reactions where there ought to be cool thinking. Such actions as arriving late and missing sessions, refusing to play or to speak, destroying instruments (though I have found this rare) or flinging them about (less rare) are irritating. Less so if the therapist can understand them. In order to do this he needs to unveil the client's negative transference (that is her repetition of earlier life situations, as a defence against remembering their distressing emotional content, by delegating the role of a hated individual, or self-part, to the therapist). Once the conflict can be brought out into

expression through music, it is easier to discuss the underlying pattern objectively.

Though it is useful to think about, clarify and enumerate aims either for music therapy or for the therapist, I would hate to think that any other therapist might commit my aims and functions to memory and feel that he should go into his sessions checking off his behaviour against them. Music therapy must be done intuitively. In musical improvisation rhythm, pitch, timbre, touch and dynamics change too fast for thinking. The therapist responds instantaneously, wholeheartedly and with conviction. When it is all over he can listen to the tape and think and evaluate his responses and lay down the foundations for different reactions another time, if necessary. But in the heat of the musical work he must feel and be and do. It is a kind of Zen in the art of musical relationship. Thinking is a crippling brake at such a time.

Having enumerated my seven rather complicated functions of a music therapist, I would like to refer the reader to Dr D. W. Winnicott's three deceptively simple aims for himself as psychoanalyst: Staying alive, Staying well, Staying awake. If mine are too complicated these would do admirably instead.

23. Inner music

Inner music is the prevailing emotional climate behind the structure of someone's thoughts. A person may not be aware of it but the manner of all his actions will quite clearly express it. It is the music of "how" rather than the "what" which will be more likely to be dictated by his head. It is this inner music which particularly communicates itself to children (especially babies), animals and sick people. Jung said, "Children react much less to what grownups say than to the imponderables in the surrounding atmosphere. The child unconsciously adapts himself to them, and this produces in him correlations of a compensatory nature." Dr D. W. Winnicott, in a lecture, told how one maternity nurse, in a hospital where he worked, always had all the babies asleep in no time after their evening feed while another never failed to produce a nursery full of screaming little miseries.

Inner music governs the feelings about those people in our lives whose relationship with us, through their work, is based on actions rather than words: dentists, chiropodists, physiotherapists, hairdressers and the like. It is the music of adjectives.

It is surprising how few exercises there are for becoming aware of one's inner music as it presents itself to the world through one's actions. As ways of endeavouring to correct it I can think of the Japanese tea ceremony, also possibly Zen, in the art of flower arranging and the family game of adjectives, where one member goes outside while an adjective is chosen and then tries to guess it as everyone answers him in the manner of the chosen adjective.

WHAT CAUSES INNER MUSIC?
Inner music is just caused by being alive and aware as a human being in the same way as is digestion or breathing or sleeping. Rudolf Steiner puts it better, "Melody exists in the soul of man. The soul is indeed the harp upon which the musician plays. The whole feeling body of man is a musical instrument on which the

Ego resounds and the soul produces the melody. It does not exist in the Cosmos. Melody lies within man himself."

Inner music is coloured by the residue of unexpressed emotion coming from habitual attitudes, emotional reactions to past events and expectations about the future. It is always there, in everyone, but it differs tremendously from person to person. Certain people have a reliable uplifting melody to which one turns in certain moods, sure of hearing the same predictable music. Others live in a poisonous fog of soured, static hate music which destroys and negates everything that they come into contact with. Most people's music is unpredictable, being reactive rather than active music, but each has his own predictable personal patterns, too. I remember a striking example of a psychiatric nurse whose pleasant inner music turned bitter overnight when her fiancé left her. The patients said that she was terrible to be with. It was not what she did, she was still a good nurse, but her physical presence seemed to poison the ward. Patients felt guilty for feeling well or contented.

CAN INNER MUSIC BE CHANGED?

Inner music can be changed if there is any willingness on the part of the owner to allow this to happen. The first step in changing it is to become fully aware of it. For example: I saw a 46-year-old widow with three children, Mrs G., who had a history of depression. She spoke curiously cheerfully about the rather gloomy facts of her life and I had the feeling that the words were like a dry crust covering something else. We did the Sand and Sounds exercise. Mrs G. sat in front of the chime bars and a tray of white sand beside a bowl of shells while I sat by the xylophone and cymbal. Immediately out came the chaotic, aggressive inner music. She viciously hit a chime bar, I replied on the cymbal while she stabbed the sand with a shell. She played two more notes, banging in between two chime bars, and then hit the existing shell in placing another near to it while I replied on the xylophone. We continued until twelve shells had been placed. The exercise clearly revealed the hidden layer of savage music which was only connected to her conscious life through the depression, otherwise she was not in touch with it at all. Its revelation was too threatening. That was some inner music which I did not get a further opportunity of helping to change.

After becoming aware of the inner music it is necessary for the client to let thinking enter this emotional realm. Where did all Mrs G.'s anger come from? At whom was it directed? These would have been the directions of our investigations had we proceeded further.

Here is another example, this time of a small but nevertheless important change. Mrs F., a phobic woman in her thirties, married with three school-age children, was slightly depressed and felt no appetite for life. This incident was from the fourth of a longer series of sessions. After speaking of hopes for a new career more challenging than those recommended by friends, she slumped back in the chair saying, "Oh, what's the use? I'm only fit for the rubbish heap." What was enclosed in this music of despair and its rejecting image? I told Mrs F. to imagine that she went to the rubbish heap to see if she could find anything of value there, while keeping emotional and musical contact with me. She played interesting two-quaver and triplet rhythms and we improvised for longer than usual. At the end she said she had found something new and shiny but she did not know what. She was hopeful and expectant and had produced this change from the depths of her own irrational unconscious, which was much more convincing than anything imposed on her from outside. At this session, too, a new face emerged, one that I felt I could work with. In later sessions she never returned to that depth of despair about herself.

AN INNER CHANGE

Sometimes an inner change comes about by bringing to the surface a festering thought which was working away beneath the level of consciousness. That was the way it was with Jane. Jane, 19, was referred to me by a psychiatrist. She was very withdrawn and had a rare metabolic disorder, one of the symptoms of which was tension. Her expression was that of a hurt child. Her verbal communication was almost monosyllabic, scarcely audible and always very docile like a very small child trying to be "good" to please someone. Her face was blank and expressionless. She was like a doll. For several months I took Jane once weekly for programmed relaxation to music.

The relaxation went well, Jane progressed so steadily that she would relax all over immediately, entirely ignoring my patient instructions. But more and more I had the feeling that her inner music was escaping me. It came to the point where I simply could not stand her lack of communication any longer. Either she drop the doll face and express real feelings or I would explode, I felt, and as that would not have been advisable, I would have to give her up.

If she would not use words then perhaps she would trust music. This was early on in my music therapy practice before the Intertherap began. I sat down with Jane in the next session and tried out some instrumental communication exercises. Each of us had a tambourine and we sat facing each other about six feet apart. The first exercise I called "Steady Flow". We were to play alternately, making the communication pattern of polite conversation; no one must break into anyone else's music but neither must there be any awkward pauses. (The value of these exercises is not only in carrying them out and noticing the irregularities, but also in becoming aware of the underlying communication patterns in everyday speech.) We started off – it is not an easy exercise – and immediately she began to come to life. There were little fierce lines at the corners of her eyes which became darker and gave me darting expressive glances. She never left a gap but she frequently broke boldly into my music and then apologised with a horrified expression. It was the first time that I had felt that there was anyone there at all.

The next exercise I called "Inward Flow"; it was the experience of being dominated. I tapped, jingled out, scratched out a short phrase and Jane was to echo it. Her echoing was not very accurate after the first few notes and she looked rather resentful. "Outward Flow" was the experience of dominating. Jane tapped and shook her motif to me and seemed to show pleasure in my faithful reproduction. So that was it. Not only did her music reveal that she had a lot to say in her own way and that she resented having to conform to anyone else's ideas, but that she was eager enough in making her contribution to break into my music rather than to risk creating a vacuum in the flow of the piece. She showed surprising dynamism.

I wanted to beckon this inner music further out into more individual expression. I wanted to bring this music into words. I had the intuition to ask Jane about poetry. This I did at the next session. Yes, she loved poetry. Yes, she would try to write some of her own.

Some weeks after this when we had progressed from tambourines to chime bars and piano, Jane produced her first poem. At last here was the kernel of the inner music which had evaded me for so long. I reproduce it with her permission.

> How can this mind survive?
> And yet a speck remains
> To revive a desolate heart
> And negative hope.

Inner music

I stand alone and try to seek
A freedom light among these deserted peaks
Or burning hell and tormented souls,
All crying for death
Among these cracking coals.

"Alone" – to stand alone
With a mind of fire and a
Throat of dried hopes is "Hell",
But yet the mind splits as if
Another is speaking of revival and cheer.

Split between freedom and pain
With voices screaming louder and louder in my brain
O God, have you such a cruel and callous bite,
That took from me the needing right:
Of sanity?

This gentle, hesitant girl had poured out her pain, despair and anger against her God for letting her have this illness. I read the poem for her, we analysed the emotional content verse by verse, and then we expressed this in improvised duets of atonal music. When we had really absorbed the feelings, we discussed the question of her illness and what special challenge it presented.

After this, week by week, her verbal communication improved. She spoke in ribbon sentences now, often initiating the conversation; she began to look more like a young woman of flesh and blood and less like a doll, and she wrote more poetry. Of course, music therapy was not her only treatment, she was also heavily supported by chemotherapy. One day she came in asking for more than her one hour of music therapy a week. I was happy to arrange this with one of my colleagues and it was not very long before she was discharged. Several months later she visited us. Her inner music sang out clear and fresh. She held her head up and looked bravely out of her eyes as if to say, "I am me and I am ready to meet the world." The inner music had changed.

ARE THERE DIFFERENT DEPTHS OF INNER MUSIC?
The inner music which I am aware of in the train is near the surface and that is why it is immediately expressed in movement or speech. However, the inner music which clients express musically is a constant source of wonder and astonishment to me. This music is frequently complementary to their conscious attitude: quiet little men produce marvellously imaginative webs of sound in which to

203

clothe their fantasies, and extravagantly emotional women settle for stereotyped rhythmic patterns to express the whole range of their emotional hypercircus. This is music from a deeper level.

With psychiatric patients, I find it difficult to experience their inner music without its direct expression. Partly because the current drugs seem to blur the vibrations and partly because the top layer of their inner music is so often the blocking barrier of non-expression, keeping their real, but unaccepted feelings far down away from consciousness. People often indicate to me that they imagine psychiatric hospitals to be wild places full of happy lunatics busy acting out their bizarre urges to an accompaniment of zany interpersonal chatter. But non-expression, inner blockages and crippling splits are the cornerstones of psychiatric illness. These are mournful places full of refugees from the fully expressive life. Even the most manic patient is having her "high" over a threatening hellhole of despair and terror where her moodswing may take her at any minute.

The best way of getting to know about these people's inner music (other than asking them to express it directly in music) is to discover what kind of climate they are allowing it to create around them. If they imagine that they are surrounded by hostile spies their inner music will be aggressive but they will experience it as outside themselves. If the therapist plays them Beethoven or Tchaikovsky, the music will come back to them loaded with the overtones of their inner music. If they are given the Rorschach test, into those meaningless black splodges will flow the creations of their inner music. To a certain extent this is true of anyone but more so of people who are dissociated from dynamic parts of themselves.

While working with a client, the therapist works down through strata after strata of different kinds of inner music. Each appears in its own time. Sometimes after a particularly good patch the psyche feels strong enough to reach right back and let go of a buried horror. This can be upsetting to the client who cannot at first understand why he should be feeling momentarily worse. Here is an example: a married man of 32, after fourteen sessions in treatment for a psychosomatic ailment which had disappeared quite quickly leaving residual anxiety to be worked through, came reporting that he had been having a recurring nightmare. He would wake up in the morning with sweat streaming down his face after dreaming he was dying. This was a clear invitation to examine any feeling he had about death. We improvised Dying. He played rather angrily on the xylophone (anger was his defence against these feelings) and I, by counter-transference, was expressing his real horror and anxiety on the piano. When we had finished, he told me that he had experienced the sinking feeling that he used to have at the beginning of his illness, but this he could accept. The next part, he said, was terrible. He had found himself in a pitch black room, looking desperately round for some friendly face to come and greet him. None came. The emotion having become conscious, he found that all the next week he was shaking, with a kind of inward quaking, but his fingers really shook visibly. However, the nightmares had stopped completely. We had dredged up the inner music of some childhood horror from a world where sirens wail and beloved parents may be suddenly blown to bits in the pitch black, friendless night.

Such a buried fear causes the whole inner music to vibrate with the repressed terror when it is released. But while energy was being diverted to keeping it encapsulated, for fear of its vibrations, this created an artificial dead patch in the inner music. After this session the client's appearance changed quite strikingly, he seemed to sink down at rest in himself, while before his head had seemed stretched up as if it feared contact with his body. His inner music lost a certain strained note and he also appeared more mature.

Working with the inner music is an important and exacting part of music therapy, an endlessly intriguing study of which the therapist can never tire. For when he leaves his work he cannot say goodbye to it, he takes his own inner music home to make or mar his private life.

24. The parameters of sensitivity

Sensitivity and insensitivity are often regarded as being mutually exclusive. Thus I regard myself as being entirely sensitive when I feel my emotional pain but you regard me as being utterly insensitive when I make you feel it. Yet no one admits to being insensitive. Insensitivity is a quality only possessed by others. But just as the Eskimos say that there is no such thing as laziness, I cannot, as a music therapist, believe that such a condition as insensitivity exists.

I was recently recording an improvisation which had the most interesting and sensitive-sounding interchange of rhythms between myself on the piano and the client, Mr M. a man of 32, on the xylophone. He started off the canonic effect by playing three stressed reiterated crotchets which I answered with three similar notes at another pitch and he answered again at yet another. So it went on, up and down, in and out, with answers being thrown back and forth. How sensitive he was to the sound of my music, you might say. Not a bit of it. When questioned he said he had, in fact, been absolutely oblivious of my music and was entirely absorbed in his sound responses to his inner world where he, in fantasy, had lit a bright torch in a dark subterranean chamber and, lighting up the walls he had stared at row upon row of skulls. Finally he found a door which he opened and through which he escaped with a sigh of relief into the fresh air outside. The therapist's musical holding in the outer world – I was acutely sensitive to his music – allowed him to flow into and partake of a musical wholeness which was a strong enough container to enable him to become sensitive to this rather horrifying inner image. I, in turn, was totally insensitive to my own inner imaginings, though having a receptor turned just enough inwards to pick up any feelings coming in by counter-transference from the client's unconscious.

So, in examining the parameters of sensitivity one sees that though, at a given moment, there may appear to be total insensitivity at the object end of the human relationship scale, viewed in its completeness one becomes aware that this is caused by acute sensitivity to emotional pain and discomfort at the apparently insensitive subject end. To illustrate: Mr L. just misses promotion after many years of expectant waiting because a younger, more qualified man has recently joined the firm. Nursing this pain he goes home and viciously tells his wife that she is beginning to look a frump with all that superfluous weight and why can't she keep herself in trim like Mrs V. next door? If Mrs L. is more sensitive to his inner pain than to her vanity she will discover the source of his hurt and help him to face the situation. If not there is trouble brewing for both of them.

One of the great values of music in therapy is its ability to allow the improvising client to be in touch with both ends of the inner and outer sensitivity scale. If she is totally taken up with sounds, timbre, pitch and rhythms on the surface, still the therapist can hold her in the inner region and respond to her there. If, as more often happens, the client is ridding herself of intensely felt emotions, she will be totally oblivious of the therapist's piano accompaniment. There is, at such a moment, nothing in the world for her but her pain and her expression of it. She is wholly submerged in this, in total sensitivity to the inner. Only after working through her pressing emotion completely with the therapist enabling her to have the whole experience of shattering climaxes and shuddering decrescendos, the client at last becomes aware of the therapist's music as the expression of another person. As she relates sensitively to this, the subsequent music can take on a delightfully playful duet character. The fact that Mr M.'s music did this without his being aware of it was partly due to his defence against his warm feelings for the therapist which were showing in other subtle ways at the time.

In life, what is needed is balance and fructifying intercourse between the inner and outer realms. Any permanent position of total subject or object relatedness, any exclusive devotion to the needs of the self or the outer world can be disastrous and self-destructive. The totally "unselfish" other-directed person can behave with what appears to be exquisite tact and sensitivity to those around him and yet, by being insensitive to the needs of his inner nature, he may – like Mr F. – achieve a psychosomatic illness whose symptomatic message tells the world, "I must be looked after" and causes others to give him the attention which he should long ago have given himself. He finally forces the outer world into giving him that permission-to-regard-himself which his early training lacked, even if it is only in the form of pills in boxes formally marked "To be taken 4 times daily" or being urged "You should look after your-self".

In music therapy, in an ordered structured situation, such a client is given authoritative permission to attend to his inner need for expression. What begins as something that might be thought of as self-centred probing develops into a truly social act through music. After 19 sessions a client in his thirties who had shed his presenting psychosomatic symptom but was working through residual anxiety, reported that he could now come home from work and instead of telling his home-based wife a few reluctant dry facts about the day's doings, he related his feelings and the mood of the workshop and made it all come alive for her by acting the various characters. He had enriched his own life and that of his family by co-operating with his inner self and his need for expression. His sensitivity balance was restored.

Another interesting kind of balance restoration comes about in music therapy. Time after time I have noticed that as soon as an emotion is being expressed, the client at once becomes in touch with all that is *not* that emotion. At this moment she is no longer identified with it, she is free. For example Mrs G., a 36-year-old librarian, had fallen deeply and rather unsuitably in love with a married colleague. The emotion having no outlet, she was quite overcome by the feeling of nebulous sentimentality. But from the moment when we spoke about improvising on it, all this was lost in the purposeful activity with drumsticks on drum and soft stick and wire brush on cymbal. Here were purpose, action, calculation, critical listening, creative imagination – everything that was needed to balance the moist and misty mood of her improvisation. In making her feeling into the fuel for legitimate action – music making – Mrs G. relieved its gaseous effect on the mind and paralysing effect on those faculties which we had used so successfully in producing the improvisation. Regarding this effect Dr Viktor Frankl says, "Emotion, which is suffering, ceases to be suffering as soon as we form a clear and precise picture of it." In forming this as a musical sound picture, it is dissipated. Not forever, but long enough to allow time to think how one can ameliorate the situation.

In the balance between the parameters of sensitivity there are unfortunately people who lose at both ends. Their inner areas are so painful that they spit out at others defensively without regard to the havoc that they are wreaking, and lose all their friends. When others, however, turn the tables on them, their defences collapse completely and they suffer long and deeply from relatively trifling psychic wounds. Their anger, coming directly from inner pain, is dangerous as it holds open the channel back to the painful spot. Anger felt as righteous indignation does not make one vulnerable in this way. Through music therapy the therapist can help the savage client to remove her defences and together they can examine the very painful trigger points. In this way her defensive anger can be freed for more constructive purposes. Dr A. H. Maslow says, "Anger does not disappear with psychological health, rather it takes the form of decisiveness, self-affirmation, self-protection, justified indignation, fighting against evil and the like."

Happy the individual who has achieved the delicate balance of sensitivity to both outer and inner areas of focus. His inner needs, once acknowledged, can be contained and transmuted into activities which will be both expressive for him and acceptable to the outer world. But this does not happen by chance. Somewhere along the line someone successfully taught him that it can be safe to let the fires of anger rage and burn out and that the waters of sorrow will not completely engulf him. Having been lovingly held in the whole experience he can trustfully accept and contain the part experiences until a convenient and acceptable mode of expression can be used.

What has been missed of holding in the past can sometimes be experienced in the present through music therapy. The music can form just as firm and reliable a holding as a loving parent's arms should once have done. To give an example: a manic-depressive professional woman in her thirties had a recurrent fantasy of an unattached living fragment of a beloved parent. Improvising on this fantasy the therapist's music enabled her to link this fragment up with the whole object in such a way that a terrible sadness, which must have been felt when the client in childhood first opened her mind to steal this object, was experienced in all its poignancy. That fantasy of the fragment did not recur again.

The musical holding can be an important factor in joining elements which have been split apart in a client's mind. A young woman, Miss R., had been unable to tolerate early ambivalent feelings of love and hate towards one loved (and hated) parent. In consequence the two feelings had to be kept apart in her world. During her early treatment her music therapist was regarded as entirely lovable and an earlier therapist was regarded as grim. When her music therapist went abroad in the summer break, Miss

209

R. gave her a St Christopher medal and suffered very much from the thought that danger might overtake her on the journey. At one point news of an accident on the continent gave Miss R. the thought that she must take her life if the therapist had perished. The destructive forces which she imagined over there were unconsciously experienced as her own and therefore she felt that she must die, too. On returning home the therapist sensed that the client had an overdue residue of the unexpressed, therefore they improvised for ten minutes on no particular subject. In the music the violent clashes on the cymbal were tolerated alongside gentle ripples on the xylophone. A beginning of the tolerance of ambivalence had appeared. Over the next three sessions ambivalent feelings for the therapist began warily to show themselves in speaking, too. The music had permitted the two feelings to be held together without danger.

The hysteric has never achieved containment: all her painful emotion is passed on ruthlessly for others to deal with as they can. This is not due to her insensitivity but to her total lack of the necessary mechanism for emotional containment and transmutation. Through finding a channel of expression in music, movement or drama, she can often be greatly helped towards finding containment in the interim periods between sessions more bearable. In conversion hysteria the emotional response to a situation is tolerated so poorly that the results of conflicts and traumatic events are passed straight from the mind to the body, by-passing the emotions completely. To illustrate: Mrs T., 27, felt violently sick whenever the moment approached for her to attend her husband's office socials. Improvising on this with the music therapist Mrs T. discovered an inner punitive mother figure furiously forbidding her to make herself attractive for these events in view of the many inviting male parent figures in the gatherings. As soon as the energy streamed into the drums it was drawn from the nausea-producing mechanism and she felt relieved but she also felt the mixture of fear and anger which had been by-passed. Of course in long-standing cases of hysterical paralysis the condition can become physically irreversible through atrophy of vital tissues.

There are people who are only unconsciously sensitive to their inner world and apparently sensitive to people around them whom, however, they mostly use to discharge at secondhand those emotions which they, themselves, feel to be too dangerous to entertain. Theirs is a team approach to expression, involving two people for the expression of the one person's feelings – a kind of keeping a husband, wife or child to bark for you. Sometimes a couple take turns to express a dyadic emotion – but this can be helpful. For example Mr and Mrs P., a couple in their late thirties with three daughters, had to break off a holiday in town to go to the funeral of his mother in the country. On the day of the sad news the wife was all strength and decision while the husband and children wept with abandon. Next morning the wife broke down completely while the husband took charge. Then again at the funeral the wife regained her composure, her strength enabling her husband to express his sorrow moderately while still being able to support his grieving father.

The apparent total insensitivity of some autistic children to the outside world can be so complete that they do not even blink if something is waved near their eyelashes. This is frighteningly combined with what appears to be an equally total insensitivity to their own inner needs which are expressed only in bizarre ritualistic movements. James, an aphasic, severely subnormal, brain-damaged, epileptic and autistic child of 12, used to search my music room for paper which he would snatch up and twiddle about. From being a defensive barrier pattern in one compulsive rhythm excluding real feelings expressed from within and also stimuli coming from outside, with musical accompaniment he seemed to channel real emotion and meaning into the actions which began to get a freer rhythm, expanding into a little creative paper game which included throwing the paper away and finding it again, all with lively squeaks of delight.

Sometimes people are completely locked when their sensitivity to their inner need for expression is equally balanced by their sensitivity to the possible disapproval of its expression by those around them. They are held in a vice that prevents any creativity or expression whatsoever, until some kind unkind person in outer reality takes away the fear of possible disapproval of expression by turning it into the experience of such violent disapproval of non-expression that the balance is disturbed and out shoots the long-blocked yelp. This was a favourite tactic of master-class music teachers and theatrical producers. It is a blunt instrument, painful and often shattering; but it sometimes works. Music therapy offers another solution. Client and therapist simultaneously improvise different sides of the problem. First the client plays the inhibiting factor while the therapist plays the will to creativity and then they reverse. When the inhibiting factor becomes conscious it is often a subject for laughter, relief and amazement. But at any rate the shift of power has come about naturally. No more need be done. The work streams ahead.

Often, what passes for insensitivity to the outer is, in fact, acute negative sensitivity. For to wound most cruelly one must be uncannily aware of one's fellow's sore spots and be able to aim with sickening accuracy and most delicate assessment of the ugliest time and place. People who do this are deeply sensitive to their own inner pain but being unable to contain and transmute it they feel that they do the next best thing by making another suffer it too. In this way a degree of negative empathy is brought about which may be the highest creative interpersonal relationship that such a person is capable of at that time. The music therapist would try to take the negative empathist right through the bitter experience of his pain until at last creative, constructive forces might begin to move in the burnt out hell-holes.

Another use of music therapy is to help a person to desensitise the exaggerated states of sensitivity. With a client who is over-sensitive to the moods of others, the improvisation can be a relationship rehearsal in responding purely to the outer sound sensations, rhythmic patterns and intervals of pitch, almost excluding reactive emotional feelings. With a client who is too sensitive to her own emotions, the improvisation can take the form of a cool sound pattern duet based on an abstract idea.

The ideal balance is achieved when the outer sounds are experienced as from an observer point as much as from the creator-experiencer angle. It is to be found where there is exchange of ideas and feelings, where inhibition of response can be a pleasure, where each stays vulnerable but creatively (rather than reactively) responsive and where each hears the other as much as himself but is also creatively aware of the unity of the dyadic vibrations. Where the parameters of sensitivity have been explored and experienced and a resting place between the inner and outer chosen as comfortable and convenient, there is peace.

25. How music therapy works

Rhythm has been scientifically proved to have either a stimulating
or depressing influence on the rhythmic systems of the body: the
circulation of the blood, breathing, heart rate. It also touches the
emotions, which of course affect these systems through the pituitary
gland. Babies put into nurseries where a heart beat sounds over the
loudspeaker system have been found to sleep longer and grow faster
than babies in a silent nursery. A newly bought puppy will usually
settle down quicker if a large alarm clock is tucked up beside it.
It is possibly for the same reason that the young examination
candidate studies to the steady beat of pop music. On the other
hand rhythmic drumming has been used to send warriors into
battle at the height of their powers or to send dancers into states of
frenzy and ecstasy. Lively rhythm is useful for breaking tension.
Turn on a lively tune in any waiting-room and notice how tapping
fingers and feet will take the place of clenched fists, crossed arms
and tensely crossed legs. Lively rhythm also has a permissive effect,
all but the most obstinately inhibited patients will dance to Latin
American and Spanish rhythms. Scottish reels and jigs are also
inviting but less relaxing. The subtle rhythms of classical Indian
ragas played on Indian sitar and tablas appeal to the higher instinct
of curiosity and usually have a quietening effect on Western people.
  Possibly it is the 1:4 ratio of breathing to heart beat that makes
quadruple time the most useful for a steadying effect. Triple, quintuple and septuple times promote a feeling of restless energy and
overflow.
  Harmony is the heart of music. It appeals chiefly to the emotions.
For this reason where there is serious emotional containing to be
done, the therapist will want to be master of the emotional scene
with a harmonic instrument such as the piano. Where this is not
available it is possible to make do with a melodica. The close semi-
tones of the atonal dissonant tone cluster make its effect more
catalytic than that of diatonic harmony. For this reason it is more

suitable for containing the inchoate inner music of emotional distress. The proportionally spaced harmonies of the major common chords soothe, strengthen and regularise while the minor chords ease sorrow and yearning.

Melody is the element which appeals most to the intellect. The flow of the notes passing in time must be held in the mind if it is to follow the melody's pattern. Tension and relaxation of pitch in melody have an effect on the physical body of singer, player and listener. One can often hear a performer on a string instrument, or a pupil, making little grunts and squeaks vocally as he endeavours to coax the melody out of his instrument. But it is not just the sound which rises in pitch, the heart and endeavour of the performer also rise to meet it and bear it up. Similarly if you now try to recall the first four notes of "Annie Laurie", you will feel something tighten in the back of your throat, and if you try to put all your feeling into the expression, even in imagination, you will notice a lifting of another kind in your consciousness.

The patterns of melodies have been born out of the life experiences of their composers. They have deep inner meaning. What meaning? As Mendelssohn said, "The meaning of music is too precise for words." I remember kneeling in front of a tiny boy with a huge hydrocephalic head in a hospital for the severely subnormal. I played him a jolly little tune in the major on my violin. No response. But when I played in the minor his eyes sought mine and his whole tiny body expressed keen attention. He was three years old, but I think we shared the experience of suffering expressed in the music.

There are four modes which I find especially useful for improvisation: the Dorian (piano white notes beginning on D), the Aeolian (white notes beginning on A), the pentatonic scale on the piano black notes and an Eastern scale going A, B, C, D sharp, E, F, G sharp, A. The first two have, for me, qualities of peace, acceptance and continuity. The pentatonic scale is cheerful and resigned and, as there are no semi-tones, duets or ensembles of players can improvise in it together without producing dissonances more shocking than a whole tone clash. The Eastern scale gives a piquant flavour of controlled frenzy and can be used with a tonic and dominant drone in the bass.

In free improvisations where the client is very emotional, it is wise to finish up with some melodic music to bring the mental functions to the fore again. This can either be incorporated into the improvisation or played separately afterwards.

214

How music therapy works

The concentration and co-ordination required in using all the different aspects of function in performing music has a sedative effect which is useful for elated patients or anyone with troubles to shed. Improvisation, especially, has a momentary amnesic effect on the player because he is so exclusively aware in the present that this cuts down all anxiety about past and future and gives the damaging brain tracks a rest.

MUSIC USED ACTIVELY IN THERAPY

When this kind of music therapy works, which is not always, it works by the power of enlightening communication. For many people music provides a guiltless vehicle for the expression of their feelings. About such symbolic representations, Melanie Klein wrote, "Representation by means of toys – indeed, symbolic representations in general, as being to some extent removed from the subject's own person – is less invested with anxiety than is confession by word of mouth." These same feelings, if expressed in words or through the natural emotional discharge mechanisms of sobbing, raging, trembling or copulating, could provoke terrible guilt and shame. But they can not only be expressed in music but also be approved of by the music therapist. In this way the therapist steps in to give that vital permission-to-be which the client may never have received in early life.

During the Intertherap (analytical music therapy workshop-training sessions), one or other of the team has often begun by saying, "I feel that it is going to be impossible for me to speak about this problem", then found that after the emotions have been poured into the improvisation, it has been a simple matter to put the formerly inexpressible problem into words. For the same reason sometimes the music therapist will begin an initial session by giving the client a small drum, and using one himself, and asking her to express all her feelings about all the things that she feels she can never tell anyone. They then begin drumming together and continue until some physical and emotional warmth has been generated. After this words flow more easily.

Psychosomatic illnesses are caused by an unhappy state of mind. Sometimes an external event may provoke strong feelings in a person who cannot tolerate them as an emotional and conscious experience. Feelings are energy. They don't just disappear, and so when the normal emotional expression is by-passed, the energy is passed on to create havoc through unconscious expression by the

215

physical body. Music therapy helps by enabling the client to take this energy back from her body and express and experience it consciously through sounds and later in words.

Here are two examples. A teacher of 42, mother and wife, came to her session with a severe headache. I asked her to show me in sound how unpleasant it was while I played her, whole and well, on the piano. Her playing was extremely violent and the improvisation quite long. When it was over she said that she had felt furiously angry with her mother-in-law who had been staying with them for the weekend. After quite a tirade against the old lady she turned to me in amazement saying, "My headache's quite gone!"

A young mother and wife, Mrs K., in a state of depression and fear coinciding with marriage breakdown complicated by a very bad relationship with mother-in-law, came to her session complaining that she vomited her food up after every meal (she was not pregnant) and the psychiatrist had only said that she did not believe it. Mrs K. sat at the xylophone and played the feelings about eating and vomiting – a lovely upward glissando. We were able to connect some of these feelings with those about her own dominating mother. At her next session she reported that the vomiting had stopped.

MUSIC THERAPY AS PLAY

Another function of individual music therapy is that of adult play. In children's play, the first step towards the actualisation of desires and hopes is taken in reality and the vital link between inner and outer forged.

Children who were evacuees in Vietnamese hospitals were quite apathetic until they were supplied with primitive toys. It seems that this bridging world of what Dr D. W. Winnicott calls Transitional Objects (bits of fluffy cloth, toys and sometimes analysts) is very necessary for creativity. In music therapy the inner world can be entered, its experiences brought out into music, the emotion shared, and when the first steps in the reality of sound expression are taken, the bridge is crossed.

This is how this worked in the case of a writer in her forties who was suffering from a creative block which was causing her great anxiety. She was asked to visualise a high wall with a door in it marked "Lay-out of the book" and go through this, keeping contact with the therapist via the instruments. Music, being dynamic, prevents the visualisation from becoming static. The improvisation was lively and varied. When it was over she told the therapist, "With difficulty I passed through the door and came to a tangled wood with animals in on the left; then a fox started up and was hunted by horsemen. To the right of the wood was a beautiful serene river which made me want to cry, and on the right of this was a green hill with a grey castle on it and a great big eagle with his wings spread out against it; then a book on a lectern."

Various aspects of the image were explored musically. One of the most vital was the lectern which kept the proposed book up in the air away from reality. She improvised Ideal and Real with the therapist, taking each role in turn. Quite suddenly she felt that it was now perfectly possible to write the book. She left the private session in a flood of released energy which she used to sweep through a queue of chores and write the chapter headings that evening. She told the therapist later that she had started writing the first chapter the next day before breakfast. The solution in this case seemed to come on a non-verbal level. It is a mistake to imagine that all realisations must be verbal. The bridge between the inner world, where the block was, and the outer, was successfully crossed with music therapy.

PASSIVE MUSIC THERAPY

In actual fact, no form of music therapy is really passive, in that the client's mind, and often the autonomous nervous system of the body, is always reacting to music, even if she is asleep. One only has to try to sleep in a tent in a field where there are animals to discover that the ear/brain recording process does not turn off during sleep. However, I term "passive" any music therapy in which the client is not actually moving to music or performing it, in however simple a way.

PROJECTION AND DISCUSSION

The most widely used form of music therapy, utilised also by Occupational Therapists, musical psychologists and psychiatrists, is to play some taped or recorded music to patients and then have a group discussion about it. Unless the patients are musicians (in which case they may analyse the composition and criticise the performers fairly objectively) they will project their feelings and fantasies into the music and it will be these that the discussion will really be about. It is quite remarkable how some patients, who are defending themselves against their own anger, can deny its existence even in a piece of music. In one group of five, three neurotic women told me that they found de Falla's *Ritual Fire Dance* "peaceful and harmonious". They were far more seriously repressed than the last two women who were able to project all their pent-up fury into the dance and were happy to admit its existence there, though they themselves had difficulty in admitting and expressing such feelings in life.

GUIDED IMAGERY

This exercise of guided imagery to music is only suitable for individual work in that there should be time to examine the contents of the unconscious symbolism and possibly to retrace the steps where an impasse has been reached. The client is given a starting point relating symbolically to her situation – for example she is to go into the forest to find something in a castle there – then the music produces the emotional dynamic stimulus that helps to unfold the symbolic situation which her unconscious wishes to reveal to her conscious mind. To the client it is rather like having a dream without sleeping. These waking dreams, handled skilfully, can have a liberating, energising effect on the client as the energy previously bound up in the unconscious symbols becomes available for conscious use. Used by unqualified people they could be destructive and dangerous.

MOOD IDENTIFICATION

This is a group exercise in which patients are told something about the music to be played and the life and aspirations of the composer, and are asked to identify with one specific mood – such as joy in such music as Strauss waltzes or the last movement of Haydn's *C major Op. 33. No. 3 string quartet*. The exercise can be very helpful in sustaining a chosen mood. However, one cannot will oneself to identify totally with a mood if one's psyche is resisting experiencing it for some reason or other. The blockage provides useful discussion material.

SELECTIVE FUNCTIONAL LISTENING

These exercises can be used either in a group, or in individual sessions, clients listening to the music while relaxing in chairs or on rugs on the floor and then discussing their experiences. The idea of the exercises is to try to use one selected function of the psyche for the duration of the music, beginning with about ten minutes and working up to twenty or thirty.

218

THINKING

This exercise is described in Chapter 31 on Therapeutic Uses of Music under the title "Music to sharpen the mind".

FEELING

This exercise is described in the same chapter under the title "Music and emotional expansion".

SENSATION

In this exercise the music is experienced as pure auditory sensation without critical or analytical thought, without reaction to one's mood or any search for meanings. Music by John Cage, Stockhausen, or any electronic music where there is variety of timbre and dynamics would be suitable, also Debussy, Ravel, Stravinsky or other composers offering rich sensuous experiences. The auditory sensory awareness experience can be followed by interpersonal tactile sensory experiences suitably structured by the therapist to suit the patients or clients.

INTUITION

Music forms a holding background in this exercise while the client alters the level of her normal consciousness. The client should have pencil and paper, and strive by lack of striving to develop that relaxed but watchful form of consciousness of inner and outer which Freud described as "free-floating attention". She waits, like a cat at a mousehole, for ideas and intuitions. When they come she should write them down. She should be welcoming and permissive to promote the inner flow, any criticism destroys the process. Even seemingly valueless intuitions can be found to possess a rich store of meaning on further examination. Moody, fluent music such as as Brahms' *clarinet quintet* is best in my experience. Discussion on the results should follow and all ideas requiring active follow-up should receive an honest plan of action.

The value in these exercises is in the client's being aware of the various functions of the psyche and of her also being aware that she is able to use them selectively to counteract their lopsided development.

RELAXATION AND VISUALISATION TO MUSIC

In this exercise the therapist goes through relaxation instructions while the group or individual client lies on a couch, reclining chair

219

or on rugs on the floor. When relaxation has been achieved he suggests a suitable visualisation for the client to hold while he improvises matching music. If there are two music therapists for a group then one can usefully observe the breathing and relaxation patterns under relaxation and give a sign to alter the music if necessary. The subject of the visualisation should be based on the material which the individual client, or the most needy member of the group, has produced earlier in the session. Some visualisations which I have found helpful are: "Imagine you pass through a door and a friend walks with you, hand in hand, in the country", "Imagine that you are surrounded by deep blue and in your centre there is a lighted candle", "Imagine that you are lying surrounded by beautiful, scented flowers", "Imagine that you are on a wonderful holiday", "Imagine that you are in a caravan trail on a journey surrounded by people whom you love and who love you (if they don't exist invent them)" and "Imagine that you are a spring of water, then a stream, then a river flowing down to the sea".

The value in this exercise is that the imagination of happy experiences acts on the brain almost as strongly as the experience of the good experiences themselves in reality, and this in turn produces in the body the best conditions for regaining health and peace of mind. It is the reverse of what happens when one worries: repeatedly visualising calamities and working up a tense, anxious frame of mind and body. I will never forget the smile on one very unhappy phobic patient's face as she lay on the floor with her hand outstretched imagining that she was walking with a friend.

MOVEMENT IN MUSIC THERAPY

The value of using movement in music therapy is both the conscious awareness of the body as an expressive instrument, and the therapist's presence giving the client the permission to use her body in this way. She needs to be allowed to own her whole body and all the sensations arising from it. As the client moves, the therapist will note the dead "trespassers prosecuted" areas of her body. She needs to be aware of what she is expressing through her body when she is disowning parts of it and its sensations, and what she is expressing when she thinks she is expressing nothing.

Structured movement

Folk dances and action dances give a feeling of belonging and being safely contained in an orderly, meaningful structure. Even the very handicapped patients, who could not dance alone, manage to hold hands in a ring with evident pleasure. This is a valuable form of social interaction for those who cannot, or will not, speak.

Exercises to music are part of music therapy only in as far as the body is being used expressively, even though the underlying therapeutic use of the physical movements may have been suggested by the client's remedial gymnast or physiotherapist. "Reach up to the stars!" gives a different quality of movement to chair-bound geriatrics from just raising their arms. Art has intervened.

Free expression

The body has its own memories bound up with its patterns of tension and relaxation. Free expression allows the client to approach these memories, free the imprisoned emotions and try out new paths of endeavour. An Israeli music therapist colleague told me how a mute schizophrenic lady was first persuaded to hold hands and sway to the music and then stand in a ring and move to Strauss waltzes. Slowly, over several months her swaying turned spontaneously to a rocking with her hands as if she were holding a baby. Further investigation into her history through the case notes showed that she had, in fact, lost her only child many years ago. Through movement she brought back this silent grief to be shared.

Some people's lives are so cramped and anxiety-ridden that their bodies have never had the opportunity of expressing natural exuberance and expansive delight. If you go into the poorest parts of any city you will see such cowed and hunched-up citizens. Plenty come into hospital. But they also come from every class, from every kind of poverty. Once they get over their initial inhibitions they find it a great release to be able to move freely and express attitudes of joy and hope through generous and expansive body movements to counteract their habitually sad, savage and anxious ones.

Part of the joy of free expression is that it has only the aim the client herself likes to put into it. As no purpose is being pushed in from outside, it is easier for some purpose to emerge from within. It is useful to follow the free expressive movement with an exchange of experiences or discussion.

26. The musical relationship

Although I have described a splendid battery of interesting and possible instruments for therapy in writing about a private music therapy practice, the means for producing a musical relationship can be extremely simple. One percussion instrument for the client –a tambourine is adequate – and a melodic and harmonic instrument, such as the melodica, for the music therapist, will do. With two such instruments carried in a small bag, music therapists have worked in sick rooms, kitchens, studies, yachts, wards without pianos and in hotel rooms at home and abroad with success. Such conditions are not ideal but they certainly allow for the possibility of a musical relationship.

The client's introduction to sound expression is a delicate business. It is essential that the client should at once be concerned solely with expressing her feelings and never at any time with trying to please the therapist or to "do it right". Apart from breaking up the instruments, there is in fact no right and wrong, only validity or invalidity of expression. Only the client herself can be the true judge of whether the sound expressed is a valid form for her emotional force, though the therapist can guess when the client is testing the medium gingerly and with his music encourage her to trust the music's capacity to contain the full measure of her emotions. In the beginning the very minimum of instructions should be given. The therapist might point out that one can obtain three quite different sounds on the tambourine by either beating, shaking or scratching it. He would probably then start with an exercise related to the client's particular problem at that moment. For example: during a lecturing visit abroad I gave a session to a 60-year-old lady, a hatha yoga expert who practised much ardent meditation, both activities which require considerable control and little expression. She told me that she had recently been medically tested and proved physically fit but that she had lately started to do several actions at a time and kept forgetting where she had put things. This sounded like the mind turning in to where there was unexpressed emotion. I told her to visualise a

222

wall with a door in it marked "How to use my emotion" and go through the door to see what was the other side, meanwhile keeping contact with me by making sounds on the tambourine. I had to be quite sharp with her to make her get down to the actual business of playing. She played with long, white fingers tentatively tapping the tambourine, then sliding her fingers across the instrument feeling it as a blind person might feel his way along a wall. There was more eager, excited tapping which my melodica accompanied with bright, shimmering chords, and finally the sensitive feeling came again but with a facial expression of rapture and tears streaming down her cheeks. When we stopped she said, "There *was* a door, there *was* a door and I just opened it a little and it was huge in there and I felt that I went through not just for myself but for all mankind. Then I quickly went out." It was a powerful, releasing experience. The musical holding of the sound expression enabled her to reach deep into her psyche and draw out this dynamic image. We later discussed its meaning for her.

The musical relationship between therapist and client, and the verbal relationship, are two quite distinct things, having totally different characters. They resemble the difference between two judokas bowing to each other before fighting in the dojo, and actually fighting, or a husband and wife discussing the garden and the same pair making love. Verbal communication can be a cold, lonely business. When one person speaks the other must be silent or his speech will annihilate that of the first. It is not a united expression like music and fighting and love-making. But if one person improvises and a second enfolds her sound expression in his own, she is instantly contained in a greater whole. She expresses herself completely and yet feels that she is a part of something greater. Aware and whole and yet a part, it is a good feeling.

The musical relationship is much more primitive and yet more sensitive than the verbal. One young woman hospital patient, given to violent suicidal attempts and running out of doctors' meetings, was seldom other than reasonable and controlled in her verbal communication with me because she knew that she would be allowed to express all her pent-up anger, terror and desperation in our very savage musical relationship.

Sometimes a client's sound expression represents a defence against true expression. This will often be a steady beat in even tempo. If this is all she can produce, the therapist can accept it and play with it, creating rhythmic patterns round it until he can cajole and musically persuade her to let some creativity through. With a seriously disturbed patient this could take many sessions.

Occasionally the musical relationship is a genuine two-person relationship. When it happens, it is delightful. The client turns to the therapist when they have finished playing and says, "I enjoyed that!" – often with some astonishment. But more often, in the initial sessions, the client and therapist's music adds up to one whole which represents the greater wholeness of the client. Either the therapist is containing an emergent feeling of the client and allowing it to grow and develop dynamically and meaningfully, or he can, by counter-transference, be complementing the client's playing with an emotion that she is not even aware that she has as it was buried in the unconscious. In his music he is giving back to her frozen or lost parts of herself to accept or reject, but to do so at a conscious level. All these experiences make useful material for the verbal part of the session.

Through the musical relationship not only is the client, by being held, able to reach back in time to free the emotions frozen there but in some inexplicable way also able to take the comfort and holding power of the therapist's present music into the past wounded condition and feel that she has been able to relive it differently. As an example a middle-aged woman client, who always became very anxious and unsettled at times when people in her office went on holiday, was told to become six years old. As she played her mournful music she saw the old family house with its large furniture and the street lamps outside and relived a feeling of intense desolation as her parents had just gone away. The therapist's warm and gentle music came into the scene like a balm and gave her enormous comfort and a sense of being loved just at that age, in that particularly overwhelming sense of sadness. At the same time her own music was holding her in the present.

Another woman, also middle-aged, had many years ago had an extraordinary out-of-body experience in a flash of extended time in between taking two steps in the street. Since then, though she had an exacting job and was perfectly normal, she had felt curiously unreal as if life were a game which everyone but her took seriously. This had been her experience. As she had walked down the street one day she felt some kind of energy bolt shoot out of the pavement up through her body, rocketing her out of it into space where she said she heard the music of the spheres and experienced herself as music. A large being came and stood silently behind her, holding

her ribs, then she came back to normal consciousness and took the
next step. I told her to go back in time and to be that being and I
would be her. She found this difficult. Then when I played the being
and she played herself of that moment, she became quite excited
and we played together for some time. This enabled the energy and
excitement split off in this experience – possibly oedipal in origin –
to join her present-day self and to be shared in reality with another
human being. It was an experience to which she had returned many
times as a ghost leaving her everyday life impoverished of emotion
and the feeling of the reality of the here and now. She said, when
we had finished playing, that it was so nice not to have to be there
all alone. We discussed what the meaning of this experience might
be for her and what obligations it entailed.

The musical relationship is not always based on inner images,
fantasies and recollections. Sometimes the therapist will put the
timer on and say, "We will play for ten (or fifteen or twenty)
minutes." No plan, no problem, no title, they just begin. The music
expresses secrets which are never explained. The therapy couple
meet in tones, timbres and time patterns and rise and fall in dynamic
development. The client knows that the therapist is there, musically,
for her; his music holds her, enfolds her, urges her on to greater
daring and holds back while she falteringly finds her own musical
form. Sometimes her music attacks. He is not killed but attacks
back. There is a sound battle, marvellous musical sparks fly. Then
stillness, sadness, gentle, wistful togetherness. And all the time
there is the instant response to all her inmost feelings. She finds that
she is meaningful, valid and creatively potent. There is an echo to
her expression: It is a very good feeling.

What is the purpose of the musical relationship? To use expression
in sound to discover, trust, share and investigate one's emotions
and the attitudes and images they conceal, which their expression
releases to the conscious mind. How does it differ from a verbal
relationship? Words are used as much to conceal as to express
feelings and there are censorships to verbal concepts which do not
apply in musical expression. When the emotion behind the verbal
concepts has been discharged musically it is easier for the words
themselves to flow.

In music, a client will often show the self she longs to be. The
mute, shy little creature will break into the therapist's phrases,
crash into pianissimos and show a musical violence that is in sharp
contrast to her verbal communication. The big, red-faced greasy-

haired insurance broker with solid, materialistic outlook will create sound patterns of exquisite delicacy and tenderness, accompanied by images of strange and haunting beauty.

A young wife and mother, 26 years old, was referred to me by a consultant psychotherapist. She was monosyllabic, suicidal and had never had the slightest enjoyment from what very infrequent sexual intercourse she had had. Verbally we got nowhere. I toiled away at the questions and became more and more bogged down by the monosyllabic replies. "They say I'm the quiet one" was her longest sentence. How different was our musical relationship. She sat like a queen in front of the instruments, clashing on the cymbal, banging on the drums, racing up and down the xylophone in response to her inner images. As the energy was released from her inner to her outer world, she could now hear for herself, on the tape playback, that she could be quite forceful and emotionally communicative in sound. It was three sessions before this began to carry over into verbal communication, and thirteen sessions before her sex life altered quite dramatically.

In the musical relationship the therapist, too, can be quite different, much more of a real person with all his feelings. He can contradict, dominate and change the mood as well as contain, comfort, reflect and complement. But in the music he cannot disguise what he really is; music is a transparent vehicle of the expression of being. The musical relationship is a very subtle and intimate way of connecting with another person's emotional and spiritual life, yet it leaves the therapy couple free and impersonal at the mental and physical levels. It is a sensitive and wonderful phenomenon, worthy of a great deal of study.

27. The encounter

"Is it the music or is it you?" is a question which observers often ask the music therapist. If they are talking about who or what cures, when cures occur, I can find no answer but the one which a psychiatrist on the Music Therapy Diploma course rather angrily gave me: "Only God cures." However, the music therapist must believe that he has some part in it or he could as well leave his instruments at once and take up more remunerative employment in a boot factory.

Dr Viktor Frankl, writing on this subject, said: "The crucial agency in psychotherapy is not so much the method, but rather the relationship between the patient and his doctor or, to use a currently popular expression, the 'encounter' between the therapist and his patient. This relationship between two persons seems to be the most significant aspect of the therapeutic process, a more important factor than any method or technique. However, we should not be disdainful of technique, for in therapy a certain degree of detachment on the part of the therapist is indispensable."

A great part of this book is taken up with describing techniques and yet through it all there will come some kind of encounter between myself, as a person, and my readers.

The encounter, or what the music therapist is to the client, is the sum total of all that he has experienced in his life, including relationships, plus his own beliefs, attitudes and the creativity with which he has responded to his life situations. If this is so important, it is worth while thinking very seriously about it.

First of all why is he doing this work? Is it for money? The status? The superior feeling of being able to help less fortunate individuals? The respectable voyeurism into the lives of others? The joy of sharing music? The intellectual interest in puzzling out patients? The fascination in following up an unfoldment of being? The satisfaction of helping someone to extract a meaning from a meaningless situation? A feeling of love of humanity focussed on each individual at a time? Love of himself in the role of music therapist? The possibility of being able to cherish his fragile self in the client? Joy in doing battle against some of the ills of the age? The sharing of musical creativity, bringing it into the reach of every client? Trying to make up for other relationships in which he feels he has been very destructive?

If there are no answers which show that he is gaining some satisfaction for himself, far from thinking what a kind, unselfish man he is, I would be very worried lest his seemingly altruistic attitude might not contain hidden poisons which in time would contaminate his therapeutic relationships. Nobody likes to feel that they are their therapist's hair shirt.

What is his attitude towards the clients? Does he view his psychiatric patients contemptuously as "either mad or feeble" like one psychiatrist with whom I worked? Does he agree with Jung and Frankl and many others that there is a part of the personality that remains in the background ever untouched by illness? Does he think that his knowledge contains the solution which he only needs to impart to the unwilling client in order to achieve success? Does he believe with Bruno Bettelheim that "No person can know what is disturbing another person, that the best he can achieve is to help another person himself to discover what troubles him"? Does he feel that the roles of therapist and client should be strictly adhered to and carefully hide his humanity behind the persona of his professional status? Does he, like Jung, think that "The crucial point is that I confront the patient as one human being to another"? How much does he need his clients' recovery and improvement to promote his own feeling of self-esteem? How much does he need his clients' trust and belief in his work to function adequately as a music therapist? How is he able to handle his angry, despairing and negative clients – in external reality and internally, in his thinking and feeling?

Whatever his attitude to his clients, this will inevitably filter their responses to him in this colour. The most sensitive and other-directed of them will eventually save him the trouble of having to filter anything out. They will obligingly become that colour.

What are his beliefs? Are humans all merely psycho-cybernetic machines programmed for failure or success by early conditioning? Is illness a meaningless and unearned catastrophe? An attempt by the psyche to achieve wholeness? An earned karmic debt from a former life? A product of the client's schizophrenogenic family? An inadequate response to an inadequate environment? Is there a God whose help and inspiration the client can invoke in his struggle

228

towards wholeness? Is the client deluded if she believes in such a Being? Is talk about such matters beyond the scope of music therapy? What is the purpose of normal, healthy life anyway? To earn an adequate income and keep out of hospital, prison and debt? To be happy? To make meaningful relationships? To be sexually fulfilled and adjusted? To develop oneself and help others to do the same? To be successful? What does this mean – climbing to the top of one's professional ladder, having the biggest car, most attentive mate, brightest children and most elaborate holidays? Or does it mean "The coming together of all this is beautiful" as the *I Ching* states? Is it necessary that one has any purpose in life at all? For oneself? For the client? Is there perhaps some other purpose, totally different?

Whatever the answers to these questions they will be sensed by the client as an intangible climate surrounding the therapeutic relationship. To take one example: If a religious client finds herself with an atheistic therapist, then she will almost always sense this, not talk about it and about one sixth of her experience, thinking, feeling and activity will not be explored at all. She will feel shut in with and cut off from sharing a large part of what she may feel as a very meaningful part of her inner and outer life. Naturally if the reverse is the case, the therapist will refrain from foisting his own beliefs on to the client but even in silence they will pervade the atmosphere of the relationship, possibly destructively, possibly creatively.

Clients can be very sensitive to the goals which their therapists, consciously or unconsciously, have for them. If these are too far below, or different from their own, a client may retain the most withering contempt for the holder of this readymade solution. If, on the other hand, they indicate a greater view of herself than she had dared to entertain and constitute a challenge to her growth and becoming, she may well be grateful – though not immediately, for first she must discover them for herself as her own.

It is useful for the therapist to review his own relationships with other professional people throughout his life and examine the impact of these various encounters on himself. I can look back and see that some people, just by their presence, have been good medicine for me. It was not what they did, it was they themselves. The climate in which they moved, possibly what esotericists would call their "aura", was beneficial to me. I looked forward to seeing them, even if their particular treatment was unpleasant, and I inevitably felt better when I left. Why was this? I have thought about it a great deal and I have come to the conclusion that it was because they were comfortable and at home with themselves that they allowed me to feel at home with myself too. They did not push their cumbersome projections on to me and make me try to fit in with them, they did not limit me with their narrow outlook of doubts and fears and they did not check off my progress against a list of goals which I did not even aim for. If they disliked something about my reality they may have said so but I felt that ultimately they left me free to live as I thought best. Most important, perhaps, is the fact that while being entirely themselves, they left ample space for my being, and their own world view and personal validity were never threatened by it, as mine were not threatened by theirs.

Is the therapist's professional self different from that self which he shows other people? Different therapists will have different answers. Personally, as the therapist I do feel slightly different from my off-duty self. As a therapist I gather myself into one firm piece and imagine that I make myself into a shape like a giant concave reflector aimed at the client. This reflector has the purpose of being able to receive as much as possible of the client while filtering out of the relationship any irrelevant thoughts, feelings and responses of my own. There is a feeling of strength and love. I do not feel that these qualities are mine but rather that I borrow them for the period of the therapy. In fact I know that they are not mine because even when I feel weak and depressed and the client is odiously unlovable, I still find that they are available to me. This may sound odd if it has not been experienced but I have described it honestly so that others can compare their own experiences with mine.

How much should a music therapist – possibly as the only therapist seeing a client regularly – feel responsible for the results of a client's frantic desire to kill herself, leave home (if she is young) or to break out of her marriage? Should he take the line of Carl Rogers: "As a seriously disturbed client wrestles with his utter inability to make any choice, or another client struggles with his strong urge to commit suicide, the fact that I enter with deep understanding into the desperate feelings that exist but do not attempt to take over responsibility, is a most meaningful expression of basic confidence in the forward-moving tendencies in the human organism"?

I think that this idea of empathy is very important indeed. I spend a great deal of time just trying to understand my clients, to see how the world looks to them and to discover, with them, their starting place. In fact the words most often repeated to me by clients have been "You understand". But, faced with the young woman who snatched up a glass, shattered it and began to slash her wrists with it, I found myself compelled to act as that part of her which was missing at that moment – I just held her tight until she dropped the glass. Far from this being a vote of non-confidence, I believe that in doing this I helped her to become aware of her greater self, by my becoming a substitute part of it; just as I might lead her around, if she were to be temporarily blinded, without showing any mistrust in her ultimate ability to see for herself.

And what about marriage desertion? I will not say marriage breakdown, as so often the client's marriage has not broken down as it never was a real marriage between two whole people. But perhaps the client had projected one of her parent images on to the marital partner and after unconsciously acting out the parent/child relationship in the marriage, she has grown up enough in the therapy to want to "leave home". The partner becomes the outworn, discarded parent and the first friendly passing male who will treat her in her new "adult" role is likely to become entangled in the triangle.

What responsibility has the therapist in all this? He can simply say, "This you must work out for yourself. Whatever decision you make, I will give you all the support I can in re-building your life", or he can treat the marriage itself as a kind of dual client – almost a sick duet. Naturally if he elects to do this he in no way takes over the vital decision as to whether the marriage has broken down or not, but he does help the couple, with the aid of music, to explore their feelings about each other, about themselves as marital partners, their ideas of the roles of husband and wife and, if there are children, of father and mother. If the other partner (who is not in treatment) feels that the therapist is concerned only with helping to assess and share their feelings and attitudes in the safe structure of the therapy hour, he will usually be more than happy to attend the sessions. The attitude of the client to her husband and vice-versa are an important help to the therapist in knowing how to proceed. He is able to point out where the husband is colluding in playing "father" and the client evading adult responsibilities by perpetuating childish attitudes. It is quite natural that in any relationship where one member is having any form of psychotherapy (among which I include music therapy) there will come a time when she has begun to gain strength and no longer is the repository for the other partner's weaknesses. At this time weaknesses may show themselves in other members of the family: attacks of 'nerves', psychosomatic ailments and conflicts are common. It is only reasonable at this stage that the client's partner should also have the opportunity of growing and adjusting with her. The change that they will have to undergo in order to adjust to each other's developing selves is less than the change (and possible working through of guilt) that would be necessary in taking a new marriage partner and in one of them leaving their children behind.

In all of this the therapist's own attitude to marriage and family life will not be without meaning. Even if he refrains from offering any advice, passing any judgement or expressing his own beliefs and values, his expression, reactions and silent attitudes to marriage, sex, society, love and duty will give their own colouring to the hour.

Finally, an important part of the encounter between therapist and client – although it can also be used as a technique – is the sharing of silence. Silences can be regarded as terrible guilt-laden chasms, as wonderful seas of expectancy waiting to be bathed in, or as havens of peace from any overt communication in which the self is discovered. I still remember one particular silence from my own analytical psychotherapy. It came around session 37. It was not one of the agonising gulfs wherein I would scowl and look at the mantelpiece and wish I was dead, nor was it a sea of expectancy, just a sudden, gentle emptiness when I realised that I was sitting across the small room from a large seated human being. It was like waking up. I looked without speaking rather as an animal might look. Time passed, I blinked. I was me. There were sounds of life in the street. Then I smiled. The human smiled back. How unbelievable. He was not me. I hadn't invented him. We were people. I heard the sounds again. The experience must have cost me about 40p. A moment later my voice plunged back into the therapeutic maelstrom and that silence was shattered never to return. I do not remember a word spoken to me during that session but the quality of that silence is a memory which is almost tangible it is so strong.

The music therapist has two specially powerful kinds of silence to share. One is the silence that comes after playing music together. I always think that this moment – in concerts – before the applause comes has a most powerful unifying effect on the audience. There is a strong realisation of "We're us. We've all had this experience together." In my own violin playing I work towards achieving this, even in hospital wards where it is so noisy. Where it happens it is always beautiful. The other special silence is the moment of concentration before the client starts the improvisation. This is the moment of the therapist's deep trust in her ability to express herself just as she will. It is his admission of his permission-to-be, to do, to express and to feel; it is his willingness for her to take the initiative. She has absolute power in that silence. In therapy I think that it is in these times of silence that the being of the therapist most subtly affects the client. He is then encountered just as a fellow human and a person who can create a complete emptiness for the being of his client to fill. Words and music and silence and experience are all part of the encounter in music therapy.

28. Strange communication

As a music therapist one is always on the alert to pick up any kind of communication from clients. It can be routine. It can be strange. It can also be quite unexpected. It was like that with Greta. One autumn we music therapists arranged to take a fortnightly session of one hour in a long-stay ward of elderly ladies. The surroundings were pleasant enough. In the lounge area there was blue lino, a red carpet, house plants, a vertical carpet loom and curtained windows. Yet it was a depressing place. Some 35 ladies sat round in armchairs, some on towels with rugs over their knees as their incontinence had given them sores. In one corner several ladies sat in geriatric chairs with bars across. One of them, the focus of my feeling about the whole ward, was Greta. She had been in hospital for some 36 years and within the last half decade had had a stroke. She was tall, with short, grey silky hair, long emaciated limbs and a face like a troubled fox. From time to time she would let out a strange animal cry, something between a howl and a moan, and occasionally slip slowly down the chair and have to be heaved up again by the nurses.

The first few times we worked there, having ascertained that she could neither sing nor take an instrument, I avoided her. It seemed quite wrong in a therapist but somehow she frightened me. Childish fears of werewolves and vampires were nearer to reality than I had liked to think possible when I left that ward. But it troubled me. Then one day I knew that I must make contact with Greta. I must find the true being in that ebbing physical body. She must have been a baby once, I thought, and had a mother who loved her. I would go there and approach her from this angle.

During the next session, while my colleague was playing old songs I took Greta's cool, leathery, saliva-dampened hands and looked into the foxy little eyes. Gently I clapped her hands to the rhythm of the music. Her arms were stiff and difficult to move but her eyes never left mine and soon the face that I had thought so sinister broke out in a lovely smile. She just glowed with humanity. After

234

that I would have a special game with Greta every time we visited that ward.

One week I came there as usual ready to play with her, but her geriatric chair was empty. I looked round. She was not there. We were fairly busy so I didn't think much more about it. But the next time, or it could have been the next after that, I asked a nurse where she had gone. "She is dying of gangrene of the back. Would you like to see her?" So matter of fact! But I suppose dying, to experienced nurses, is what changing a violin string is to a music therapist. I followed her. There in the huge dormitory, the white bed clothes humped off her lower limbs, lay Greta. She was curled up with her eyes closed, her face had a mauvish hue. The nurse said, "I've brought someone to see you, Greta," but she didn't move. I touched her forehead gently with the back of my fingers. She opened her foxy eyes and let out her animal cry. The nurse talked to her for a while and Greta looked at her. This nurse had often taken Greta out in her wheelchair and had become very fond of her. When she stopped Greta looked at me. I said, "Goodbye, Greta," then, as a flood of music came in from the ward, "Can you hear the music?" She looked me straight in the eyes and a radiant smile lit up her face. Its effect was such that the nurse gasped. Had Greta understood me? Did she connect the music with our games? It was a beautiful goodbye. She died before our next visit.

Replacing Greta in the ward came a foreign lady. Some nurses said she was Italian, some Polish, French and even Arabic. Actually she was French and two of her schizophrenic children were also long-stay patients in the hospital. But she didn't respond to words even though they were shouted into her ear as though she were deaf. She was not deaf, but she was blind. Formerly we had been used to seeing her up on another ward where I had been worried because she repeatedly wiped her nose on her petticoat, lifting up her dress and revealing that she had no pants on. It wasn't that it upset our male voluntary assistant so much as that I thought that it was undignified for her. I felt that as she was blind and unaware of herself we should be guardians of her dignity as well as her physical well-being. Were there no hankies? Or, failing that, no pants? Get on with the music. It wasn't our worry. In this ward she seemed to have been cured of her perpetual cold but appeared to have decided that life was not for her. She sat with head down and arms folded like a roosting bird, reacting to nothing but the nurse propelling her to and from the dining areas four times a day.

During the old songs I went up to her and touched the backs of her hands to present myself. Her hands clasped mine like a greeting. All her life and consciousness met me through them. We swung up and down to waltzes. We bounced jauntily to polkas. We firmly beat time to marches. I tried just letting my hands be passive in hers. Was all that rhythm and life really coming to me from her hands? It most definitely was. She could hear the music, appreciate the rhythm, change direction from up and down to sideways without any direction from me. But this was not the limp, passive movement that other patients gave me. I had the feeling of being in touch with a person of passion and a great love of life. What had happened to turn her completely off?

Another strange communication came to me when I was taking a regular session at a psychiatric day centre. Once weekly I gathered together in a bleak and dreary first-floor room with from eight to fifteen patients who were not ill enough for hospital but not well enough for life. We had two hours for music, from two to four, and so I used to let the time pass more enjoyably for them by sometimes inviting friends of mine to come and play or sing. On the afternoon I am speaking of, a young photographer friend brought his vina along. He wasn't an Indian himself but was studying with an Indian guru. The patients sat in a semi-circle on hard chairs with that careful, narrowed posture that comes from trying to look absolutely normal when you feel far from it. They seldom said anything but they watched the large string instrument with its shiny gourd resonator with interest. Among the patients was Leah, a young Jewish woman who always appeared half asleep or drunk, whether from drugs or alcohol or both I don't know. She was naturally very artistic and was a welcome addition to the singing when she was able to come downstairs for it.

The first two pieces on the vina were announced and played and duly applauded. Then the photographer began to improvise and at once Leah, who had seemed barely conscious, took up a strange chanting. The tones of vina and voice mingled harmoniously and the music flowed on and on in tortured sadness and despair. Leah's dumpy body sat totally relaxed, eyes shut and head leaning backwards like a great frog, pouring out this marvellous, mournful sound. Was she functioning from some deep strata of the collective unconscious having its origin in the Far East? Or was she just too drunk to have inhibitions and too doped to have doubts, never singing a note wrong? Gone was the dingy room with its bare

236

board floor, the poster about a teacher's earnings and the three appalling gift pianos. Gone was the therapist/patient relationship. We were all transported mentally to the dusty streets of an Indian village. We listened enthralled. It was most moving. When they stopped, I said, "What was that?" Leah opened her eyes and looked at me, astonished. "I don't know," she said.

29. Transference and counter-transference in music therapy

Contrary to popular opinion the transference is not a sinister device invented by Freud to cause patients to fall in love with their analysts in order that they may attend their sessions regularly and keep paying the fees. In fact, in the early days of psycho-analysis the transference was regarded as a rather unfortunate and obstructive side-effect of the business of making the unconscious conscious. Later, it was understood to be a vital and therapeutic aspect of the process of psycho-analysis.

Transference can be described as a process by which a patient attempts to relive with her therapist the unfinished business from former important relationships in her life. It can also be her attempt to come to terms with, or rid herself of, conflicting parts of her psyche by projecting them on to her therapist.

However, transferences did not come into the world in 1912 with Freud's recognition of their value. They have, of course, been experienced under different names since the beginning of time. Nor are they restricted to the analytical relationship. They flourish between pupils and teachers, students and tutors, actors and actresses, confirmation candidates and curates, patients and GPs, dentists, social workers, and every kind of therapist, customers and shopkeepers, hairdressers and chiropodists, clients and solicitors, stockbrokers and accountants – whom have I missed out? Therefore it is in everyone's interest to know something about them.

Where analytical work is being carried out, the transference is usually much stronger and involves deeper feelings, probably from an earlier, sometimes pre-verbal, stage of life. The reason why these feelings are re-experienced in the present is just because they were so strong and painful when first experienced that their memory is resisted. Instead of the feared memory the unconscious produces a compulsive urge to repeat, in the present, the situation which first evoked them.

What does this feel like when it is happening? Rather like walking in a chin-level river before you can swim, with a lifeguard sitting on the bank giving no instructions and then telling you what happened when you have stubbed your toe. You struggle against it until you learn that you might as well resist growing your finger nails. Then again it is rather like being pregnant; it just goes on and on until the end is accomplished. It is hellish having the unwieldy great child-feelings to battle with at the same time as having to lead an adult, responsible life, but then there are wonderful moments of insight and clarity and relationship which make you feel that it is all going to be worth it.

Where the transference is projected on to a psychologically qualified person, the difference is that it has a fair chance of being received objectively and examined and interpreted in terms of the transferer's past relationships. In this way it is possible for the repetitive cycle to be broken and for the transferer's situation to change. When the transference is projected on to an unsuspecting lay person, he is likely to find himself unconsciously responding to what is expected of him and being unwittingly forced into playing the role which the transferer gives him; at the same time often feeling inexplicably embarrassed and helpless in the situation.

In the professional analytical relationship, because of the understanding of the situation, the transference can begin to be dissolved as soon as it comes into being. In the lay situation, unless there is great wisdom and insight, the repetitive cycle may simply reinforce itself, sometimes in a very destructive way. This kind of mechanism is in operation when a woman goes through a series of disastrous love affairs or a man repeatedly loses jobs through quarrelling with those in authority over him.

POSITIVE AND NEGATIVE TRANSFERENCE

Where warm, loving feelings are directed towards the therapist, the term positive transference is used. Freud described this as one of the energetic sources of healing. It is within this warm relationship that the patient makes use of the interpretations that will help her to help herself.

The resistance to positive transference is the projection of feelings of hate, fear, anger and resentment on to the therapist. About this Dr H. Racker writes, "The knowledge, for instance, that behind the negative transference and the resistances lies simply thwarted love, helps the analyst to respond with love to this possibility of loving, to this nucleus in the patient however deeply it be buried beneath hate and fears."

It is the therapist's work to resolve negative transference as soon as it appears as it blocks further progress.

TRANSFERENCE AWARENESS AND THE MUSIC THERAPIST

Is it necessary for the music therapist to know about this? Is superficial knowledge enough? If the music therapist is going to work solely with severely subnormal individuals then a superficial knowledge of transference and counter-transference, as obtained from reading, will probably be all that is necessary. In working with other clients, if the music therapist has a stable personality, plenty of intuition, common sense, reliable advisers and an awareness of the transference process, he will also manage to do his work satisfactorily. If, however, he intends to do analytical music therapy, work on his own in private practice or to specialise in psychiatric work, then a deeper, individual experiencing and dissolving of his own transference is of great value through analysis or analytical psychotherapy. Together with this, a parallel course of Intertherap (musictherapy workshop-training sessions) is advisable to discover ways of using the arising emotional situations musically from the point of view of both client and music therapist. So far, analysts have accepted this arrangement quite agreeably, even feeding material back into the Intertherap for musical exploration.

COUNTER-TRANSFERENCE

This term is confusingly used to mean two different things. The first is the therapist's transference of projections on to the client. This is not useful and is, in fact, destructive of the therapeutic relationship, if it gets out of hand, as it then becomes just like any other relationship with the client being forced into a role of the therapist's choosing. I do not mean this definition when I speak of counter-transference.

The second meaning is most important for music therapists as they use it all the time in the musical part of their work. It is the therapist's identification with unconscious feelings, self-parts (instinctive self, rational self or conscience) or internal objects of the client, which, being conscious in the therapist, can serve him as a guide to the client's hidden inner life. How does he know whether he is really receiving the true message or imagining it? Dr H. Racker here says, "According to my experience, the danger of exaggerated faith in the message of one's own unconscious is, even when they refer to very 'personal' reactions, less than the danger of repressing them and denying them any objective value."

To some music therapists these messages have an overwhelming and mind-numbing quality. I am one of them and our problem is in not over-identifying with and being overwhelmed by these transferred feelings. To others these messages are like an elusive, still small voice to be listened for acutely. When he is improvising with clients these counter-transference feelings leak up from the unconscious almost as if they were the therapist's own. Being unconscious, their primitive quality makes them difficult to deal with. But awareness and practice can make a useful tool out of what threatens, at first, to be a dangerous disturbance. The musician has his mind wide open when he improvises and it is at this time that he becomes aware of feelings that he did not notice during the verbal preamble. It is essential for the music therapist to divide himself inwardly into an inner, detached observer, who can objectively review counter-transference intimations, and an open, irrational receiver who can turn them, or their opposite, into sound patterns. But with one ear on the client and two hands on the piano and an awareness of the flooding counter-transference, it takes a great deal of practice to preserve this observer intact.

EXAMPLES OF COUNTER-TRANSFERENCE DURING MUSIC THERAPY SESSIONS

Here is an example of a kind of musical positive resistance to counter-transference. With Mrs B., private client, 32, married woman and mother of three, as soon as I started to improvise on the piano, with her at drum, cymbal and xylophone, I was always filled with a paralysing feeling of inadequacy. Her improvisations were hesitant and short but their inner realisations were vivid and meaningful. One day I accepted the load of inadequacy as usual while playing through a dream with her and then I thought, "This inadequacy doesn't belong to me. I am ridding myself of it." I pushed it away from me from inside. My playing flourished. Mrs B. seemed to catch the reversed flow and her playing was richer and more confident and lengthier than ever before. I have tried this reversed flow many times since with success.

This is an example of trusting the inner intimation. I was taking a session with Mr F., 32, who had been telling me earlier about his fear of interviews and he mentioned in passing that he always just said, "Mother believed dead" (his mother had left the family when he was quite young) brusquely when asked. I asked him to imagine a high wall with a door in it marked "The Question I Cannot Answer". He started playing with light, anxious taps on the xylophone. After a minute or two the counter-transference intimation made me play deep, rolling, harp-like chords in the Aeolian mode. A little rational, argumentative voice in my head asked why I was doing this, it was so different from his music. I didn't know but I was trusting my intuition.

His inner experience justified my intuitive musical response. He had opened the door and entered a graveyard and he was on his knees going from one stone to the other pushing back the ivy leaves and searching for a name which he could not find. My music sustained the solemn background to the situation which his conscious mind had just pushed aside but which his unconscious had brought him up against in all its solemnity. I was playing the deep, sad music from his unconscious that told us that he was afraid that his mother might be dead.

If the music therapist is not aware of the counter-transference he risks experiencing and becoming swamped by its projections because he does not realise that they do not belong to himself and takes them guiltily on himself. Or, if he thinks that they are nonsense and represses them totally he cannot be usefully empathetic to the client. The key sentence for the observer is: "What is she making me feel?" and then taking a conscious stand regarding this. Often in the middle of an improvisation the therapist can feel the client's anger somehow surge up in him and out of his fingers on the keyboard. It is an extraordinary sensation because it is so strong, and yet, not being consciously evoked, it happens in a way that disturbs the conscious mind. One never has that feeling when playing structured music in a concert, however fierce the dynamics, because the music is then filtered through the ego. Nor does one have it when improvising alone or with colleagues. It is the receptivity to the client's need that opens this unconscious channel between client and therapist.

DIFFERENCE BETWEEN THE TRANSFERENCE IN ANALYSIS AND
MUSIC THERAPY

In music therapy the client very often experiences through the music an emotional confrontation with a part of herself from which she had been split off. Once the door is open through her experiencing the feelings by means of sound expression, she will begin to admit and own them. They are there, she can hear them over and over again on the tape. She cannot deny their existence any more.

The loving feelings of the music therapy positive transference do not have the same frustrating aim-inhibited quality as they do in analysis. To play music together and, even partially, to relieve physical tensions in this way, can be an unconscious symbolic equation for various basic impulses such as feeding, making love or even killing. Music therapy transferences are therefore deep but more manageable, both in their positive and negative aspects. At the first sign of negativity the client is encouraged to act out her feelings of hate in an improvisation, and nine times out of ten by the end of the music she will burst out with the realisation of the person to whom the anger really belonged. Acting out being welcome in the music, negative feelings are usually volunteered or described rather than acted out in other than musical ways: "I felt I didn't want to come today. I felt you wanted to make me suffer", and "I didn't want to come today, I felt that you were my strict grandmother and I was hiding in a tree." In such cases it is useful to let the client be, in music, the awful therapist, while the therapist plays her. In this way she gets in touch with her projected feelings and can own and discuss them.

DON'T MUSIC THERAPISTS EVER HAVE ANY REAL FEELINGS
OF THEIR OWN FOR CLIENTS?

I have discovered that if I cannot find something to love in a client, I cannot work with her. Most of my colleagues say the same. At the beginning of a course of music therapy I feel that I am working with the client as if I were panning for gold (as I did once as a child in Arizona): filling the pan with dry river sand and shaking it until the heavy stones and gold dust come to the surface. When I've seen the glimpse of gold – and it may be in a drum beat, a rhythm, an expression, a gesture or a stray sentence – then I know the way ahead is clear. I am happy. Later, perhaps I will lose sight of the gold and have to start panning again. But I've seen it once so I know it is there.

It would be impossible to improvise with someone unless one had a great deal of empathy. The music therapist cannot hide his feelings behind a veil of objectivity like the analyst. Sometimes they are there in music, rumbling, tinkling, thumping, trilling and cascading all over the place. He holds the drum beat with tenderness, he pounds it with rage, he lulls it with dreamy harmonies, he brings it to shattering climaxes and shuddering depths. He sweats and grunts. Sometimes he dabs his eyes. He cannot operate as a therapist-shaped blank annihilating memory and desire. He works as a fellow human being, travelling his path as swiftly, honestly and valiantly as he knows how. He cannot be more and tries not to be less.

30. The meaning of music

When Mendelssohn ~ ¹⁴, "The meaning of music is too precise for words", he was sayi. .ich the same thing as Stravinsky when he said, "Music has absolutely no meaning." Yet it is important for the music therapist to realise that music – his working tool, with its rhythms, fluctuating dynamics, changing harmonies and flowing melodies, is a fundamental attribute of all existence. Scientists are discovering that rhythm and vibration are at the basis of all manifest life, t'   ~ʰ what we .an actually hear and see constitutes less than a millio.. ᵗ of the inaudible sound and invisible light. I realised this dramaʋically when, sitting among the interdisciplinary psychiatric hospital team watching a micro-film of the beginning of a human life, the non-pulse rhythm of the expanding and contracting cells became for me a music so powerful that tears came streaming down my cheeks.

Thinkers from other cultures have expressed similar ideas in different ways. "The whole creation is a mantram (sound prayer) vibrated by God," an Indian yogi said, speaking of Nada Brahma, the Sound Absolute. The Qabalists, too, say "The universe is builded on music" and attach great importance to sounding the words of power so that the human body turns into a vibrating, living instrument through which to contact the forces invoked. Though music, medicine, religion and magic have long ceased to be one profession, nevertheless the music therapist need not think of his working tool as being an alien art form cultivated separatively in the hot-house atmosphere of musical colleges and academies and quite outside the mainstream of the daily round. The elements of music are in all life.

MUSIC AND SOCIETY
The musician performs a service to the group consciousness with his music by constantly connecting and re-connecting the dissociated emotional and spiritual elements to people dried up by the trivialities of the daily round. He has access to the collective streams of cons-

ciousness and can give emotional nourishment, through a conscious musical experience, to those people who have cut off all access to their own unconscious emotional strata. What is acceptable as culture, and can even be wept over quite respectably, is not always acceptable as direct emotional experience in reaction to a turning point or break in a relationship, for example. The musician, with his music, can act as the leader of a guided tour into inner emotional territory. Safe because it is structured, the way has been signposted and trodden by thousands of others, nevertheless it is still an adventure.

However, the music therapist needs to be continuously watchful as to which type of music he is working with, assessing a group's need for either control or release. As he improvises together with his client, he will judge whether Dionysius or Apollo is the influence most needed at the moment and react accordingly.

MUSIC AND THE COMPOSER, LISTENER OR PERFORMER

For the composer, whether amateur or professional, writing music is a valuable exercise and he strengthens himself inwardly by building these sound patterns to express and share his feelings.

For the listener, music can have two different functions. Either he will try to listen to it so closely that he becomes a kind of human sympathetic string attuned to its harmonies and melodies, vibrating at a lesser dynamic but at the same rate as the composer, or he will let his conscious mind idly follow the music and free his inner censor so that he projects his own frozen emotions and unconscious images on to the music as a screen, and it, in this way, gives back to him a part of himself that was lost, so that he feels richer and more alive after a concert. An experience which many concertgoers will recognise.

For the performer, music composed by other people provides him with useful self-discipline and efforts to attune his emotional pitch to theirs, but it affords little help to him in finding his own centre and means of creative expression. On this subject Dr R. Assagioli says ". . . music can, and often does, have injurious effects on the performers themselves, who are subjected to a combination of harmful elements: muscular and nervous fatigue as a consequence of intense technical study and the excessive quantity of music, both heard and performed; the anxiety caused by public performances; the particular contrast of psychological attitudes required by the performance itself, which demands on the one hand perfection of technique, concentrated attention, and self-control; and on the other an emotional identification with the mood expressed by the music, needed to produce that warmth of expression, that powerful suggestion which fascinates the audience.

"For these reasons performing musicians need, more than anybody else, to train their will, to control their emotions and to help themselves, or be helped by a judicious use of relaxation and of all available means of psychotherapy."

I cannot agree with Dr Assagioli about will and emotional control. If anyone imagines that it takes no will-power to practise an instrument for six hours a day for five years or more, as a solo instrumentalist must during his training, then they have surely never tried it for themselves. In performing, a musician has his emotions under tight control, even when releasing them to the full in the music. What he does in his private life is another matter. But I fully agree with Dr Assagioli that relaxation and psychotherapy are extremely valuable in helping the performing musician to find his centre. Particularly the psychotherapy of music therapy, in which he will combine the instant creation of his own musical forms with the binding of the emotion through discussion with the therapist. To one trained to release his feelings in the rich, colourful, non-verbal medium of music, mere talking seems to lack something as a completely satisfactory means of expression; it leaves an uncomfortable physical and emotional residue of the verbally inexpressible.

MUSIC AND THE CLIENT

Many of my clients, although musically uneducated, find their musical improvisations a very powerful medium for expressing emotions that they had never been able to express in other ways. Despite the fact that my piano "holding" is often atonal and offers them few landmarks, when I play back the improvisation that we have just made on the tape recorder, they will guide me through the chaotic confusion of sounds saying: "That's where I went into the room, now I am looking about to see who is there, that is me discovering the dwarf – here he's attacking me, I'm taking his sword – no, this is that bat – now it turns into a snake . . ." and so on. This never fails to impress and astonish me. Also one particular client (who does not seem musically to invest all that much emotion in his music) is so gripped with emotion when his music is played back to him that frequently this produces temporary psychosomatic symptoms.

For some clients their music acts as a kind of emotional blood-letting which offers an emergency outlet for pressing feelings that they might otherwise disperse by acting out in less harmless ways. In this structured setting the feeling can also be shared, wild deeds imagined rather than carried out, and later spoken about with the therapist. If the therapist tries to get these clients to make music on a constructive, positive theme they feel it as a desperate constriction, cannot invest any emotion in it and find that this is merely a painful damming up of their pressing need to rid themselves of their wild and angry feelings. Their music has a compulsive quality and yet it brings them a measure of relaxation and peace.

For others their improvisation reaches levels of emotion which are bound up with symbols and images, these rise to the conscious mind as the threatening emotion is expressed, and are accepted and investigated.

Other patients, again, find in their music a new kind of exploring, a sorting out in their minds the difference between subject and object. Through this music, which represents their own personal inner world, they discover a real self which can then begin to distinguish the not-self which had been imprinted on it by others. The feeling of communicating from this inviolate self is new and valued and can gradually carry over into their spoken communication and actions.

Naturally, with most clients these inner feelings and realisations are accompanied by increasing pleasure in the whole cycle of expression from emotion to physical sensation and also a growing awareness of the sounds themselves as their own creations.

MUSIC AND ITS UNCONSCIOUS MEANINGS

To the unconscious, music often stands as a symbol of the expression of feelings through the medium of sexual activity. A schizophrenic girl spoke to me of how as a small child, the sounds of love-making from her parents' room were experienced as ". . . the most beautiful bubbling music". This explains the otherwise unaccountably hysterical shyness of some young girls about playing their instruments in front of anyone, though their performance is perfectly adequate and they would never show the same bashfulness if asked, for example, to demonstrate their knitting or how they set their hair. The often reiterated words: "I couldn't do it in front of anyone" reveal that their music is not yet being thought of as a communication of feelings from one person to another, as in intercourse, but that it is still experienced at an emotionally masturbatory stage, as a pleasant but solitary exploration. This attitude soon passes when they are encouraged to play chamber music.

This also sheds light on the recurrent question as to "Why do so many musicians grimace and screw their faces up as if they were in the last stages of orgasm while playing?" The intensity of emotional expression, being incompletely expressed through their playing, comes out partly as facial expression. It is this shared intensity of physically expressed emotion that underlies both sex and music.

Music can also represent the negatively seductive side of the unconscious, drawing a person away from the reality of his duty into a world of dreams and fantasies. Stories about the haunting fairy music, calling men out into the hills to get lost in the mist, or the dangerous sirens luring seamen to their destruction on the rocks, are all moral tales to the music therapist. He must always make a point of helping clients to extract their outer-life purpose from their unconscious fantasies and images, and not just let these draw them deeper down inside themselves till they lose all power of decision and action.

The positive use of music, in the story of Orpheus, can be taken as a picture of the fully developed man, with his whole spectrum of the emotions perfectly tuned, being himself an instrument of wonderful power through the externalisation of his vibrant inner music.

The story of the Pied Piper of Hamelin shows how this power can be used for growth or stagnation. In his black and white costume the Piper pipes the rats out of the town relieving the distress of the people. But when his request for payment was refused he piped all the children away.

In just this way the rejuvenating influence of the unconscious can be cut off from those who refuse to respond to the needs of their whole selves. The music therapist and his client must often follow the trail of the Piper to reclaim these hidden powers of growth and strength.

MUSIC AND TIME

The most important feature of music, from the point of view of therapy, is its existence in the dimension of time. Because of this there is always the possibility that the feelings of a client will undergo a change. This change may not be musically impressive but it may still be enough to convince the client that her feelings in the real life situation will be able to change, too. For example: a woman in her forties, wearily carrying on a battle with her teenage son, came to express this with me in therapy one day. What she thought was going to be pure, unadulterated hate turned out as starting off as hate then turning to anger, to sadness, to despair, to apathy, to calm and then to gentle hopeful renewal. At the end of the long improvisation she could discuss the problem of how to tackle the relationship much more hopefully and calmly, and later reported that she was able to see his point of view much more clearly.

Music, a pattern of sound vibrations sculptured in the fourth dimension of time, has as many meanings as we give it. For some it is the rich language of emotional experience reflected in their successful human relationships. For others it is a substitute experience guarding them against the need to have any but the most superficial of verbal communications. This can be one reason why sensitive children wish to take up music, they no longer trust the trickery and non-expression of words. But if they are to become music therapists they will need to break through this barrier to fully expressive conversation or they will not be able to help their clients. The therapist must find the music in words and the words in music and search all his working life for the meaning in both.

31. Therapeutic uses of music

People who have heard that I am a music therapist often come up and tell me that they, too, use music therapy: they go and bang on the piano when they come home frustrated after a difficult committee meeting. I am all in favour of letting off steam in this way, especially if they are good friends with their neighbours and their piano tuner. But it is not music therapy. Therapy means healing or caring, and so for real music therapy you need a therapist, a client and music.

However, there are many ways in which music can be used therapeutically by adequately functioning people. With its help they can alleviate stress, fertilise the creative powers of the mind, rise above the tyranny of daily trivialities, enrich their emotional life and relax the body by releasing static emotion or by control.

In some of these exercises one is musically active and in others musically passive but active in other important ways. Despite the fact that in the latter one may appear to be doing absolutely nothing but lying sluggishly in a reclining chair, these are really strenuous exercises and should be worked at cautiously, only once a day at first.

ACTIVE THERAPEUTIC MUSICAL EXERCISES
The noblest exercise of all is the playing of chamber music. Not only body, emotions, mind and spirit are used, and fused, but there is also the interaction between the players at both verbal and non-verbal levels, all of which bring real renewal and the relinquishing of everyday cares in the creation of a mutual sound world. But this is for the skilled musician, whether amateur or professional. For the other active exercises there is no need to be a practised musician. Very simple skills and instruments will suffice.

FINDING YOUR PLACE
This is an exercise to bring steadiness and a feeling of harmony and physical well-being. Use a small drum with no ridge around the head, such as bongos, an African skin drum, tom-tom or Moroccan

pottery drums. Sit in a quiet place with the drum between your knees and begin to beat it with your hands at the speed of your pulse. Realise that your beat is part of the intricate microcosmic rhythm which keeps your body alive. Elaborate the rhythm but keep the basic beat going. Realise this rhythm in relation to the macrocosmic rhythm of day and night, winter and summer and the births and deaths of stars and moons. Go back to the basic beat, realise yourself as a macrocosmic being to all the tiny atoms within you, whirling round in their own contrapuntal rhythms. Elaborate the rhythm again while keeping the basic beat. Come back to the basic beat. Stop. Realise that the other rhythms continue. Remember this from time to time during the next hour.

TENSION RELEASE

This is an exercise to release physical tension. It usually causes greater awareness of the emotions behind this tension and this is why you are asked to make it the first step in a chain of actions. The second step being to investigate the reasons why you feel as you do. This exercise has been found surprisingly effective in removing certain types of headache. Sit where you will be undisturbed. Place a pencil and paper near you. Take your hand drum and put your whole awareness into your tension. It will be agony. Then BE the tension and express the feelings of its grip on your body on the drum. Let all your tension flow into the drumming. In a short while you will find that your arms are glowing and exhausted long before the emotion is spent. Continue drumming at a speed you can manage, elaborating the rhythm until you are enjoying it for its own sake. When a creative approach has been established, stop. Use the creativity to deal with the cause of the tension, answering the questions "Why was I so tense?" and "What am I going to do about it?"

OVERCOMING FRUSTRATION

This is a melodic exercise. Use a recorder, flageolet, Indian or Japanese six-hole pipe or melodica. Some people find that they can use their voice for it. Sit where you will be undisturbed with your instrument and feel keenly the imprisoning limitations of your circumstances. Without thinking too much, start to improvise. Let your consciousness enter the sound completely, being carried up and down at will. Lean on the sound. Float on it right out of your prison. When you return it will not be the same.

Therapeutic uses of music

For these you will need a couch or reclining chair, and a record player. The choice of music will be your own as this is a very personal matter, but I give examples of music which I have found useful both for myself and with clients.

Music as tranquilliser

Choose a relaxing piece of music. The slow movements of Mozart's *Clarinet Quintet in A* and the *Clarinet Concerto* in the same key and Delius' *On Hearing the First Cuckoo in Spring* are good examples. The sound is liquid, the lines flowing and easy. Recall to mind some place where you felt very peaceful. Put on the music, lie back, close your eyes and imagine that you are in that place. Breathe deeply, sink down with the music and enjoy the inner surroundings. Let sound and place merge, with yourself as meeting point. Make a mental journey into each part of your body to find out if it is perfectly relaxed and comfortable. Go back to your peaceful place and dream. After carrying out this exercise successfully several times you will begin to connect the sounds with the inner picture and the feeling of relaxation. Later on, in between music sessions you can use the picture and the memory of the melodies to induce that relaxed, peaceful feeling in a break at work, on the train or standing in a queue. You will have created your own tranquilliser, quite without side-effects.

Music and the release of aggression

This exercise has proved useful in cases of tension, in sudden anxiety attacks and choking sensations. Any situation, in fact, where the aggression is being directed inward against the self. The music chosen should be extremely violent. I favour Bartók's *Fifth String Quartet*'s first movement. Put on the music. Lie back, legs slightly apart, arms away from your sides. Use the violence of the music to arouse your fury against anything or anyone, known or unknown, who is impeding the smooth flow of your life. Visualise yourself as enormously powerful, striding round and crushing and destroying any inanimate objects that get in your way. I say inanimate objects as even imaginary live objects can retaliate in a most frightening manner. After some minutes of clubbing and stamping you will find that you are breathing much more deeply and that you may have the impulse to flay with arms and legs If so, give way to it. When the music stops you will be dynamically relaxed, ready to

253

tackle any job which you have been avoiding. After the music and inner action have been successfully connected, this exercise, too, can be done as required to alleviate panicky sensations.

Music to sharpen the mind
This is an exercise for getting back into a working mood after a holiday, after too much emotion, after a bout of being vague and intuitive, or simply ill. I like to use the fugal last movement of Bach's *Brandenburg Concerto No. 4 in G.* It is contrapuntal music at its most exhilarating. Put on the music, relax, close your eyes to cut out visual distractions and prepare your mind to grapple actively with the music. In this music the conscious I – the ego – is firmly in the saddle. One is never overwhelmed or carried away, one does not put oneself in the position to experience inner images; the music is experienced strictly in relation to the listening ego. One listens, thinks, follows, judges, compares, criticises or analyses.

To preserve an alert, interested form of listening, allow the attention to move from voice to voice as the different instruments enter. Let the mind pounce aggressively on each entry and hang on to it. When all the entries have been made, attend to the bass and follow it until there are more entries. From the bass line one gets a rich, full textural impression of the music, having both a satisfying awareness of the harmony and also the intriguing interplay of the polyphony.

If you find your mind blankly balking at trying to take in all the music at once, let go and hang on once more to one part, or aspect of it, that takes your attention. Feel that the listening is an active, almost aggressive feeding process in which you take part voluntarily, choosing to take in now one part and now another. Do not feel yourself to be a passive victim of the invading flood of sound. Will the music to be there, give it your permission, mentally, to make its stirring crescendos and powerful double fortes.

Consider the timbre of the strings. Would that part sound better if it were on wind instruments? Consider the tempo. Could it be improved by being a trifle faster or slower? Consider the dynamics. Could they be altered to create a more dramatic or less disturbing effect? How is the intonation? What is the effect when the basses take up the subject? Fill your mind with eager questions: "How is the composer getting that effect?" or "Which part has the subject now?" Follow the rhythmic patterns without regard to pitch sometimes. Always hang on to some aspect of the music which takes your special interest.

When the exercise is over continue to feel this positive, aggressive form of thinking and apply it to other matters.

Music and emotional expansion

This is an exercise for times when you feel dried out by too much thinking, checking, comparing, deciding and verbal precision. The object of its performance is to experience emotionally. The soaring first movement of Brahms' *First Symphony* is my favourite stimulus music at present. Yours will probably vary from month to month according to your emotional needs.

Put on the music, lie back comfortably with closed eyes and feel every note with the composer. He had to live and struggle and suffer to write this. Be with him empathetically. In daily life we are always having to cut off, ignore and diminish our emotions in order to keep going. Now, use the music to help you to feel as poignantly or exultantly as you are able. Feel right into your visceral regions, through your breathing, your heart beat, your genitals, your spine, your fingers and toes. If you succeed – even imperfectly – when the music stops you will feel ennobled, enriched and lifted to a better level of being.

Music and the success experience

Here is an exercise for those who are seeking success in some areas of their lives but dare not think about it openly. This is limiting because the idea of success is a strongly motivating factor in its attainment. This exercise brings to the surface the inner obstacles to success. Samuel Barber's *Adagio for Strings* with its long, slow string tunes rising to one magnificent climax is the most suitable music I have found.

Before you put on the music imagine the successful situation you would like to attain; feel yourself into it and place it, in imagination, at the top of a mountain. Now put on the music, lie back and, knowing that success lies in wait for you at the summit, begin to ascend the mountain. If you come up against insuperable barriers, note them, and be content to wait till they pass, keeping a clear vision of the prize at the summit. If they won't move, finish the exercise then tackle the barriers in the Release of Aggression exercise. If nothing impedes you, go to the top and experience the success situation vividly at the climax of the music.

This exercise can produce a great deal of negative feedback in the way of moods of doubt and despair, but this is only bringing to the surface what was formerly unconscious. If you persist, this will pass and you will find yourself moving towards the success situation through your actions and attitudes. It is naturally assumed that you do not choose a success which conflicts with the reality principle or your own fundamental ethical code, as this would produce a dangerous conflict in the mind.

Music and physical work

Work songs, which bring the labourer into touch with the deep collective unconscious strata of his being through shared rhythmic body experience with the group, were once used to step up production and raise the workers' morale all over the world. These days the rhythm of the machine is the background music for much work, and it is bad music: angular, agitated and ugly. Piped music is little better because it is totally dissociated from the movements being performed.

If you cannot find some music with the right rhythm to work to, then create an inner tune to a beat which fits the task, and rhythmically and harmoniously work to this, refusing to make tense, anxious and jerky movements. Be music with your body as the instrument. Feel the music flowing right through your limbs and trunk. Work easily with weight and balance. Useful working music is Latin-American rhythm, any collection of work songs, sea shanties or farm songs, and, for lighter work, Strauss waltzes.

The body as instrument

For this exercise you need privacy, floor space and music. The body is an expressive instrument all the time, responding to outer stimuli and our own inner music. More often than not this is repressive and crippling. Inner parent figures are eternally telling us to "Hurry up!". The body is being used mercilessly as a machine for getting things done. Sooner or later we have had enough, we need to use our bodies in another and more friendly way. If we are lucky this may be swimming or playing tennis or making love. If we are less lucky it may be being ill. This exercise provides another way, a chance to be a totally expressive and creative instrument.

Choose any music you enjoy, preferably wordless, and pick a dance title which is meaningful to you. Some examples of titles which I have found useful are: Yes, No, Why not . . .? How can I . . .? Rejected and Accepted, the ten divisions of the Emotional Spectrum (done one at a time), Chaos/Order, Imagination/Reality, Examination, Meeting and so on. Whether you have your clothes on or off is up to you but most people find that an air bath is very refreshing and helps them to leave their persona or role mask behind. Put on the music, keep the title in mind and just move as you will. Enjoy the non-utilitarian movement. Probably you will find that ideas and feelings well up and ask to be expressed. Go with them, however irrational. The music makes a holding matrix that will not allow things to get out of control. The feelings that seek expression may be very violent as there is a body memory of former tensions residing in the muscles and this can be freed when the same movements are felt again even if it is forty or more years later. But the natural dynamics of the music will lead you, letting boiling crescendos be followed by gentle diminuendos and guiding the dance. This is a most valuable exercise to do before an examination, meeting, lecture, formal party or interview. If you are ill or crippled, the exercise can be equally valuable done through imagining how you would dance if you could. The imagination has a strong effect on the physical body, even in inaction.

LISTENING TO MUSIC FOR THERAPEUTIC REASONS

To change a sad mood, go into the sadness with serious music and then turn towards something lighter. To break tension – unless you are a master at relaxation – use very rhythmic music that will encourage movement in the body. In moods of stubborn anger and bitterness choose a triple, quintuple or septuple beat. Overcome anxious dithery moods with duple or quadruple time music, preferably from the eighteenth century.

These are just a few specific therapeutic uses of music for the adequately functioning person. Naturally I would also include learning an instrument, playing in orchestras and small ensembles, singing in choirs, madrigal groups or alone and just listening to music for its own sake either at home, in a club or at a concert.

DANGEROUS MUSIC

Not all uses of music are therapeutic – think of the numbers of people who found their formal piano lessons so destructive that they gave them up vowing never to touch the instrument again. Nor are they without danger in that they can confirm moods of helpless emotionalism and passivity or ugly, vicious insensitivity. They can stun and overstimulate the nervous system, cause partial deafness and even produce musicogenic seizures. If there is doubt as to the value of your own proposed therapeutic use of music, of if you run into any difficulties with the exercises in this chapter, it might be wise to consult a qualified music therapist.

32. The future

As increasing numbers of music therapists are trained, there may be possibilities of work for them in as yet untouched areas. It will be up to the music therapists themselves to see the opportunities inherent in the conditions of their contemporary society and to prove that their art is able to be of service in these new ways. At present several possibilities present themselves.

SCHOOLS

If all maladjusted behaviour is a potential communication, then in so far as the communication locked in the behaviour is not satisfactorily understood or received, the behaviour will tend to repeat itself. In a class with 30 or more children it is impossible for the teacher to do more than endeavour to suppress unwelcome behaviour in order that peaceful conditions for learning may prevail for the majority of her charges. The wayward child may not be disturbed enough to merit the services of a Child Guidance Unit, nevertheless this child could possibly benefit from having the help of a qualified music therapist. The communication inherent in her behaviour might prove to be about such matters as a new baby sibling's arrival, the illness of the lone parent, the parents' separation or divorce, a new step-parent, fears about unassimilable sexual or other information, a recurring nightmare or simply the fear of being unable to live up to educational expectations. All schools from kindergartens to sixth-form school, as well as universities, whose students already have a high rate of psychiatric referral and suicide (eleven times the national average at Oxbridge), could be usefully in touch with a qualified music therapist working alongside the medical staff. Such preventive work, if financed by the State, should well repay itself in the long run in avoiding set or escalating patterns of emotional disturbance. These can usually be more easily helped when they are in the fluid state of fresh emotion.

259

FAMILY GROUPS

Following on to the idea of help for children in schools, comes the idea of using the whole family unit, with a music therapist, as a words-and-music-communication group to explore their interaction and their feelings about this. The family most often functions as a work group with its own complicated interacting system, busily engaged in getting things done, seldom having time and the deliberate focus of "feeling what it's like to be us", as when they are reducing tensions through sound expression and being able to relate in a creative play setting symbolically as well as in words. Some families experience this special awareness of their interrelationship on the annual holiday, others never. The family, as the unit of society, is not yet outmoded and such a powerful influence on future citizens is worthy of help and attention when it is needed. When it breaks down without sufficient help more than one generation may suffer and society be the loser.

ANOTHER DIMENSION TO ENCOUNTER

At the time of writing, teams of isolated young people, and office and even hospital staff, are getting to know one another in a more physical and emotional (rather than intellectual) way through the use of Encounter techniques. One has a different attitude to the Matron, the manager or the office boy, when one has stood writhing back to back with them letting this part of the body express one's feelings about their backs or has sat face-to-face gazing into their eyes for a full five minutes. However, even this leaves one aspect of their being – their inner music – largely unexperienced. I have had colleagues with whom I have both worked and experienced encounter techniques, but I never felt so much real respect for them and such a wish to cherish and guard their essential selves as I did on experiencing their inner music. Here, they revealed something beautiful, sensitive and fragile that made all their rage and pain and frustration understandable and tolerable. I would not wish to add to it, having experienced this side of them.

The musical encounter group can be used to work out the problems and feelings of individuals within a group. The music gives them the advantage of an entirely primitive yet sophisticated non-verbal mode of expression and response. This allows even the shyest individual to get in touch with and express her feelings about group members, or the internal objects which they sometimes represent, and gives all the members a shared symbolic representation of her inner world in their outer reality which can then be clothed in words.

Work teams from offices, factories, hospitals and so on, groups of single people with communication problems, any group of people who feel that they would benefit from exploring the unconscious communicational current between them and discover the humanity behind the hierarchy can make use of the musical encounter group.

PREPARATION FOR PARENTHOOD GROUPS

There have long been classes in exercises and relaxation for pregnant women. It was thanks to such classes in Copenhagen, run by a doctor-and-wife team, that my husband and I experienced with satisfaction the natural births of our own three sons (two of them twins) years ago. But the arrival of the first baby is often a peak time of distress for husbands and the preparation that they need is not so much physical as emotional. There may be room for carefully led words and music communication groups for prospective parents, bringing up such emotionally charged subjects as parental roles, jealousy of the new family member, fears about adequacy in the new roles, mutual support felt to be necessary, possibilities of abnormality in the offspring, the couple's own parents as models or anti-models, sex during pregnancy and after childbirth, the feelings of being trapped in the house with the baby and so on. The ensuing relaxation should be done to the same music each week or fortnight and the parents could use this on tape at home for their daily half hour and later during the early part of the wife's labour. Though this might sound superfluous to a healthy, young prospective father, he might come to value his proficiency in relaxation very highly if a lusty infant starts keeping him awake during the night screaming aloud its disgust with the way this world is run. Naturally the music therapist leading such a group would require extra studies in this field and would be closely in touch with medical colleagues.

COMMITTEE MEETINGS

Anyone experienced in committee meetings will be aware of how they operate on two levels, verbal and sub-verbal, and how much the sub-verbal level, with its pencil tapping, doodling, chin jerking, cheek twitching and ring fiddling, can dominate the verbal level where the actual work is done. Self-assertive members, charged with mounting irritation from a frustrating day, can use the meeting as a receptacle for emotional off-loading thus paralysing their weaker fellows who never muster the courage to break through their frozen fear and subsequently leave the meeting without producing such valuable, positive contributions as they may have had to offer.

Though realising that the average committee member would find the following suggestion fantastic, yet I offer it seriously in case some enlightened person should have the courage and enterprise to try it as an experiment. A music therapy words-and-music session, with a skilful leader, held half an hour prior to the committee meeting could serve to break the inertia barriers, discharge much tension by expressing the frustration and fear, tune the members to a common group awareness and then take them forward into a state of mind that is inducive to that fertile interaction with the unconscious which is essential for all creativity. After free sound expression under qualified guidance, the whole rhythm of interpersonal communication in a group can change in a way that is quite remarkable.

PERIPATETIC MUSIC THERAPIST TO GERIATRICS

Older people tend to lose one by one the outlets for expressing emotions pleasantly – sport, intimate friendships, artistic activities, and the working interaction but have no diminishing need for them. Speaking of this a fiery old widowed lady demanded of me angrily, "Do you really imagine that I am less of a passionate person now at 80 than I was at 35 when I used to play the solo part in Brahms' *Violin Concerto* with a symphony orchestra?" No, I didn't. Such unexpressed feelings, kept within the body, encourage all kinds of aches and pains. The inner world, too, which the analytical music therapist explores with his clients, is a rich source of meaning and adventure when sight becomes blurred and mobility diminishes the possibilities of external journeying. I would like to think that one day peripatetic music therapists would be employed to go round helping to light up the lives of some of these older members of society by giving them a form of expression in sound and words adding dignity and purpose to their rich store of years and breaking down their isolation from the rest of the community.

THE USE OF MUSIC THERAPY IN PERSONALITY TESTS

Music can be a valuable aid in personality tests both as it is often used already as a projection test – the subject listening to certain sounds and dynamic patterns and instrumental interaction and saying what she has imagined meanwhile – or used actively as a holistic test playing with one or two music therapists in order that her patterns of dynamics and interaction may be studied, such as blocking expression by compulsive beating, murdering the whole performance with sound, taking or avoiding initiative and so on. The use of the Emotional Spectrum test, described in an earlier chapter would also make a very interesting study. I know at least one hospital where it is already a routine event for the music therapist to be called in alongside the psychologist when personality tests have to be made. I have been surprised and delighted by the inner music of so many unpromising seeming subjects that I cannot but feel that such testing could offer a unique and unusual exploration of certain kinds of potential which might otherwise go undetected.

THE TESTING OF MUSIC THERAPY

It is encouraging to see such an eminent psychiatrist as Dr Anthony Storr recognising the value of this kind of therapy. In his book *The Dynamics of Creation* Dr Storr stresses the importance of creativity in connecting the inner and outer worlds. "There is always something unsatisfactory and even dangerous in possessing an inner world which is utterly unconnected with the outer world." He also talks of the measured ego-strength of creative people: "Dominance, self-acceptance, responsibility, self-control, tolerance, intellectual efficiency are among the traits measured by tests of ego-strength; and it will no doubt surprise those who think of creative people as long-haired dreamers to realise that they rate highly on all these measures."

Further on he emphasises the point that such symbolic resolutions and satisfactions are open to all and that research into this subject is desirable. ". . . In mental hospitals, art therapy, music therapy, and occupational therapy are used increasingly; but they still tend to be treated as poor relations, mere adjuncts to the therapeutic ministrations of the psychiatrist. If the point of view advanced in this book is accepted, it follows that a great deal more attention and research will have to be devoted to such ways of encouraging symbolic resolutions of emotional problems. This is especially so in the case of the poorly endowed. Genius can make its own way; the gifted may need no more than encouragement. It is those who are not so gifted who need help and teaching."

In its present stage of development, I would describe music therapy as an art. Later on, its results may possibly be tested and measured and analysed so that it can be regarded as a science.

Thoughts around music therapy

Psychologists tell us that all change can be measured, and it may be useful to suggest some of the changes which I think, from my limited experience, might be expected to take place in some of the patients taken for individual analytical music therapy.

  freer verbal communication
  more constructive use of aggression, both internally for self-development and externally in useful end-gaining processes
  some reduction in psychosomatic symptoms
  better human relations
  more motivated and purposeful approach to life
  more creative approach to life
  more awareness of emotions but less unconsciously driven by them
  increased spontaneity
  better toleration of frustration of emotional expression until suitable outlets can be used (not if treatment is stopped early)
  better sleep
  some reduction in obsessions
  some relief in frigidity or impotence
  better toleration of negative emotion in others

This does not mean that every patient will be expected to show all these changes but rather that it should be in these directions that one or more changes might be looked for or expected in any given patient.

However much I would like to see the results of this art subject to any kind of useful test, I cannot believe that it will ever be an exact science. The variable of the human music therapist, whose whole being and experience and philosophy of life play such a great part in the treatment, would seem to be too great to make any such tests generally applicable.

FINALE

Well, this is the end of the book. Every day that goes by brings in more strange and intriguing examples of the inner explorations of clients which it is too late to include. Every week brings more interesting questions from groups to whom I have spoken and involved in sound expression experiments. It is too late for their answers, too. But I hope that I have given you a picture of a way of work that ploughs a sturdy furrow somewhere between the starched white coat of the highly trained medical man of today and the ragged fur wrappings of the shamans and drumming healers of other times. We owe a great deal to both. I hope, too, that for some

264

people I have pointed a finger into the future. Perhaps towards a track to be followed by some loving young musicians. To them I would say that music is our bridge, the magical meeting point between people. Relationship is what this art is all about.

I began with music. I finish with relationship. What is one without the other?

Bibliography

JULIETTE ALVIN, *Music Therapy* (London, John Baker, 1966)
- *Music and the Handicapped Child* (London, Oxford University Press, 1965)
ROBERTO ASSAGIOLI, *Psychosynthesis* (Psychosynthesis Research Foundation, 1965)
H. G. BAYNES, *The Mythology of the Soul* (London, Rider, 1969)
BRUNO BETTELHEIM, *Dialogues with Mothers* (Glencoe, The Free Press, 1962)
- *The Empty Fortress* (Glencoe, The Free Press, 1967)
AARON COPLAND, *Music and Imagination* (Harvard University Press, 1952 and also Mentor Books)
HENRY DICKS, *Marital Tension* (London, Routledge and Kegan Paul, 1967)
S. H. FOULKES and E. J. ANTHONY, *Group Psychotherapy: The Psycho-analytical Approach* (Harmondsworth, Penguin, 1957)
VIKTOR FRANKL, *Man's Search for Meaning* (London, Hodder and Stoughton, 1963)
- *Psychotherapy and Existentialism* (London, Souvenir Press, 1970)
ERICH FROMM, *The Sane Society* (London, Routledge and Kegan Paul, 1958)
E. T. GASTON (ed.), *Music and Therapy* (New York, Collier-Macmillan, 1968)
E. P. GRAMLICH, (1968) 'Recognition and Management of Grief in Elderly Patients', *Geriatrics*, 23-87
C. G. JUNG, *The Archetypes and the Collective Unconscious* (London, Routledge and Kegan Paul, 1959), Vol. 9, Part 1
- *Memories, Dreams and Reflections* (London, Routledge and Collins, 1963)
MELANIE KLEIN, *Contributions to Psycho-Analysis* (London, Hogarth Press, 1950)
A. LOWEN, *Love and Orgasm* (London, Staples Press, 1966)
P. NORDOFF and C. ROBBINS, *Music for Handicapped Children* (London, Gollancz, 1973)

Bibliography

HEINRICH RACKER, *Transference and Counter-transference* (London, Hogarth Press, 1968)

R. ROBERTS, *Musical Instruments Made to be Played* (London, Dryad, 1965)

CARL R. ROGERS, *Client-centered Therapy* (London, Constable, 1951)

ROSAMUND SHUTER, *The Psychology of Musical Ability* (London, Methuen, 1968)

LIONEL STEBBING, *Music, Its Occult Basis and Healing Value* (New Knowledge Books)

ANTHONY STORR, *The Dynamics of Creation* (London, Secker and Warburg, 1972)

RICHARD WILHELM (ed.), *I Ching* (London, Routledge and Kegan Paul, 1960)

IRVIN D. YALOM, *The Theory and Practice of Group Psychotherapy* (New York, Basic Books, 1970)

Index

Breathing—*cont.*
  and relaxation, 81
British Society for Music Therapy,
  9, 41, 47
Bush, Alan, 47
Busotti (modern composer), 49

Cage, John, 49, 219
catharsis in group movement, 81-2
chamber music
  improvisation, 29
  therapeutic value, 107, 251
child development, Klein's
  schema, 18-19
children
  autistic, 44, 211
  educationally subnormal, 42
  maladjusted, 43, 259
chime bars, 47, 52, 61
Chopin, F., 49
collective unconscious, 18
committee meetings, facilitation
  by music therapy, 262
communication
  non-verbal, 15, 140-1, 234-7
  verbal compared to musical,
    223, 225-6
composition, therapeutic, 106
conditioning, operant, music and,
  17
contact, physical, of therapist and
  patient, 62
contemporary music, 47
creativity, 31
  and ego-strength, 263
  in music and art therapy, 110-11
  repression of, 223-4
  and therapist's aim, 194-5
  and Transitional Objects, 216
Crufts, Adrian, 47
cymbal, 38, 39, 51, 194

Dallapiccola, Luigi, 49
dancing
  and expressive movement
    with long-stay mental patients,
      59, 62
  and manic patients, 68
  and repressed emotion, 77

"death", improvisation, 204-5
Debussy, C., 219
  String Quartet in G Minor, 49
de Falla, M., *Ritual Fire Dance*,
  193, 218
Delius, F., *On Hearing the First
  Cuckoo in Spring*, 49, 253
depression
  and anger, 200
  and suppressed energy, 68-9
depressive position (Klein), 19
desensitisation, 17
development, human, 11, 18, 51
dreams, 36-7, 134-6
  "waking", 218
  in improvisation, 37-8
dulcimer, 52
dumb children, 42
"dyadic unit", 153

educationally subnormal children,
  42
ego-strength and creativity, 263
emotional growth, 14
emotions
  acting out, 19
  as assessment tool, 149-50
  conceptual model ("spectrum"),
    146-8
  expressed in body movement, 77
  fixed patterns, 91
  "frozen", 224
  guilt-free expression of, 215
  and musical harmony, 213-14
  and music therapist's repertoire,
    47
  recording technique, 148-9
  and symbolic resolution of
    problems, 263
enantiodromia, 35
encounter groups, 260
encounter situation, 227
  psychodynamic movement as, 77
  psychotherapy as, 11
energy, suppressed, 68-9
evocative music, 49

family group and music therapy,
  260

fantasies, dancing and, 77
fear in emotional spectrum, 146–7
"Feelies", 80
Fink, Dr D. H., 12
Fiocco,
  Allegro in G, 66
  Arioso, 66
foetal position, 64–5
folk music, 48, 49, 220–1
Foulkes, Dr S. H., 90
Franck, César, *Violin Sonata*, 108
Frankl, Dr V., 208, 227, 228
Freud, Sigmund, 18, 24, 51, 88,
  219, 238
Fromm, Erich, 110
frustration-releasing exercise, 252

geriatrics, 45, 262
gifted children, 44
Gilbert and Sullivan, 49
glockenspiel, 52, 195
gong, Chinese, 52
Gramlich, Dr E. P., 148
gramophone records, 49–50,
  93–4, 217–18, 253–7
Granados, E., *Spanish Dance*, 60
Group Analysis, Institute for, 37
group curative factors (Yalom),
  82–3
group music therapy, 87–92, 194,
  260
group work
  in mental illness, 75, 76
  in movement and relaxation,
    78–81
Guildhall School of Music and
  Drama, 9, 23–31
guilt, 13, 47, 50, 147, 215
guitar, 25, 50

Handel, G. F.
  Allegro from the Seventh Suite,
    24
  Arrival of the Queen of Sheba,
    100
handicapped persons, 43
harmony, 213–14
Haydn, J., *String Quartet Op. 33
  no. 3*, 218

Head, Michael, 47
"holding" technique, 121–3
Hopkins, Anthony, *For Talented
  Beginners*, 24
hospitals, *see* psychatric hospitals
human development, 11, 18, 51
hymns, 48
hysteria, 210

I Ching, 229
illness
  music therapists attitude to,
    228
imagery, guided, 130–4
imagination, musical stimulation
  of, 94
improvisation, musical
  "Anger leading to Peace", 24
  atonal, 27–31, 79
  chamber music, 29, 30
  "Death", 204–5
  drumming in, 37–8
  "Fear", 28
  in Guildhall examination, 24, 27
  with maladjusted children, 43
  melodic and modal, 214–15
  "Rejection", 84
  "Volcano", 85
  "Wind", 91
  see also group music therapy
Indian music, 50, 236
inner music, 199–205
Institute for Group Analysis, 37
instruments, choice of, 42–5, 50–4
Intertherap (musical therapy
  training groups), 33–4, 35–9,
  215
intuition, 219

Jacob, Dr Gordon, 47
Jacobson, Dr E., 12
jazz, 47, 49
jealousy and group improvisation,
  88
joint sessions, 153–61
Johnson, R. Sherlaw, 47
Joubert, John, 47
Jung, C. G., 18, 35, 228
  archetypal idea, 90

271

DATE DUE